Thank you...

... for purchasing this copy of Reading for Literacy for ages 8-9. We hope that you find our worksheets, teachers' notes and display materials helpful as part of your programme of literacy activities.

This Reading for Literacy book is part of our growing range of educational titles. Most of our books are individual workbooks but, due to popular demand, we are now introducing a greater number of photocopiable titles especially for teachers. You may like to look out for:

READING FOR LITERACY for Reception
and for ages 5-7, 7-8, 8-9, 9-10, 10-11

WRITING FOR LITERACY for ages 5-7, 7-8, 8-9, 9-10, 10-11

SPELLING FOR LITERACY for ages 5-7, 7-8, 8-9, 9-10, 10-11

NUMERACY TODAY for ages 5-7, 7-9, 9-11

HOMEWORK TODAY for ages 7-8, 8-9, 9-10, 10-11

BEST HANDWRITING for ages 7-11

To find details of our other publications, please visit our website: **www.acblack.com**

ABOUT THIS BOOK

As with all our photocopiable resource books we have kept the teachers' notes to a minimum as we are well aware that teachers will use their own professionalism in using our materials.

At the start of each Unit we list some of the National Literacy Strategy Objectives that the Unit may cover. We are grateful to the Department for Education and Skills for their permission to quote the Objectives.

Some of the Units are linked to others as indicated by their titles.

Many Units feature reading activities that can be undertaken individually or in a small group situation, alongside the teacher or support assistant.

Some Units could be copied on to Overhead Projector Transparencies for use with a large group or the whole class.

The Units vary in their level of difficulty and teachers will match Units to the ability levels of the pupils in their classes.

Most Units are four pages long. All of them provide worthwhile activities as well as useful practice for tests.

Extracts from the National Literacy Strategy Framework for Teaching, © Crown copyright 1998, reproduced by kind permission of the Department for Education and Skills.

Contents ...
Year 4

Contents ...

Contents ...

Term 3

The objective indicated on the contents pages, is the main focus for each Unit. Each Unit can, however, be used for many different objectives and further suggestions of objectives are found at the start of each Unit.

This unit addresses the Literacy Strategy:
Term 1 objective   1: to investigate how settings and characters are built up from small details, and how the reader responds to them.
Term 2 objective   1: to understand how writers create imaginary worlds, particularly where this is original or unfamiliar, such as a science fiction setting and to show how the writer has evoked it through detail.
Term 2 objective   2: to understand how settings influence events and incidents in stories and how they affect characters' behaviour.
Term 2 objective   3: to compare and contrast settings across a range of stories; to evaluate, form and justify preferences.
Term 2 objective   4: to understand how the use of expressive and descriptive language can, e.g. create moods, arouse expectations, build tension, describe attitudes or emotions.

Name _____   Dreams Toyshop

Dreams Toyshop

The purple pig on the top row winked at Zel as she entered the shop. She pointed her selector module at it and watched as it floated smoothly down to her.

She examined the pig carefully, noticing it had a speech function and a music pack, but decided it really wasn't the right present for her brother's eighth birthday. Zel cancelled the select setting and the purple pig floated gently back to its place on the tenth level next to the dancing horse and the octopus that could knit.

Zel wanted to get just the right present for Sek, and she knew that the 'Dreams Toyshop' was just the right place to find something truly unusual. She gazed around the shop. It was like being inside a giant ball. The walls themselves shone brightly, changing colour every few minutes. There was every sort of toy that you could dream of, floating in rows around the outside walls or piled into enormous, swaying towers throughout the room.

Hundreds of toys were drifting through the air, some sparkling or glowing as they made their way silently to the excited children who had 'selected' them. It was just like the skymotorway around the cities, and the amazing thing was that none of the toys ever collided.

Zel scuttled about, selecting and examining, but never quite satisfied with anything she looked at. Her brother, Sek, was a very serious boy, but with lots of imagination. Zel was sure he would get very quickly bored with the 'View World' games she had looked at. He would find it fun for a while to step into another world as if you were really there, but Zel knew that these games repeated themselves after a very short while and Sek would lose interest. She wanted a present that would make Sek use his imagination.

A 'select assistant', in her shiny uniform, asked Zel if she could help her in any way. The assistants in 'Dreams' were all 'chipped' to the main computer, and only had to think of a particular toy, and it would float down to the customer. Although Zel needed help, she wasn't sure that she could explain what she had in mind.

"S-s-something imaginative please," she stammered - she always had trouble getting her words out when she was nervous, "that doesn't r-r-r-repeat itself."

"Ah yes, I know just the thing," the assistant said.

As she continued talking, Zel noticed a tiny dark cube weaving its way across the shop towards her. The assistant explained that you only had to switch it on and clasp it in your hand. Then it was up to you. You could become a part of whatever you imagined. The experience would be different every single time, and would fulfil all your dreams.

Zel knew straight away that this was exactly the right present for Sek. She stared into the paymachine, which instantly read her eye pattern and transferred the money from her bank to the shop.

Zel clutched the cube, and hurried out of the shop. She thought she heard the assistant saying something about telling her brother to be very careful about what he imagined, but Zel was far too excited to take too much notice.

1. Where do you think this story is set?

    _____

2. Which details help you to identify this shop as rather special?

    _____

    _____

3. The last sentence gives us a clue about what might happen later in the story.
    What sort of thing do you think might happen?

    _____

    _____

4. Write a short paragraph changing the setting to a toyshop today. Describe how
    a boy goes in looking for a present for his brother. What does he see on the
    shelves? What is the shop like? Try to use some imaginative adjectives.

    _____

    _____

    _____

    _____

    _____

5. The author has not described any of the smells or sounds in the 'Dreams Toyshop'.
    Write a sentence about one smell or one sound that you might find in this setting.

    _____

    _____

6. Describe another character you might find in this setting. Remember it is an
    imaginary future world, so you can make up anything that fits into the setting.

    _____

    _____

    _____

7. List four different settings that you have found in stories you have read.

    1. _____

    2. _____

    3. _____

    4. _____

8. Zel cannot always get her words out when she is speaking. Why do you think
    the author made her like this? How does it make you feel?

    _____

    _____

    _____

    _____

9. What else do we know about Zel's character?

    _____

    _____

    _____

10. Which of these settings matches the extracts below? Write the correct setting on
    the line below each extract.

    (**A disco**)   (**A space station**)   (**A farm**)

    (**A classroom**)   (**A football match**)   (**The seaside**)

    The pig rolled lazily in the sun watching her new family snuffle amongst the leaves.

    _____

    The seagulls shrieked overhead as the wind chased the clouds across the sky.

    _____

    "Science," said Tara. "Great, that's my favourite lesson. Wonder what we will
    be doing this week."

    _____

    The lights flashed purple, green, yellow. The sweaty bodies jumped and swayed
    to the music.

    _____

    The crowd roared, then a wave of chanting surged round the stadium.

    _____

    "Power on."
    "Check."
    "Fuel levels OK?"
    "A bit low, Captain."   _____

This unit addresses the Literacy Strategy:
Term 1 objective   1: to investigate how settings and characters are built up from small details, and how the reader responds to them.
Term 1 objective   2: to identify the main characteristics of the key characters, drawing on the text to justify views, and using the information to predict actions.
Term 1 objective   3: to explore chronology in narrative using written or other media texts, by mapping how much time passes in the course of the story, e.g. noticing where there are jumps in time, or where some events are skimmed over quickly, and others told in detail.
Term 1 objective   4: to explore narrative order: identify and map out the main stages of the story: introductions ➤ build-ups ➤ climaxes or conflicts ➤ resolutions.
Term 1 objective   5: to prepare, read and perform playscripts; compare organisation of scripts with stories - how are settings indicated, story lines made clear?
Term 1 objective   6: to chart the build-up of a play scene, e.g. how scenes start, how dialogue is expressed, and how scenes are concluded.

| YEAR 4 | UNIT 2 | Sheet A | Name | Storm at Sea (1) |

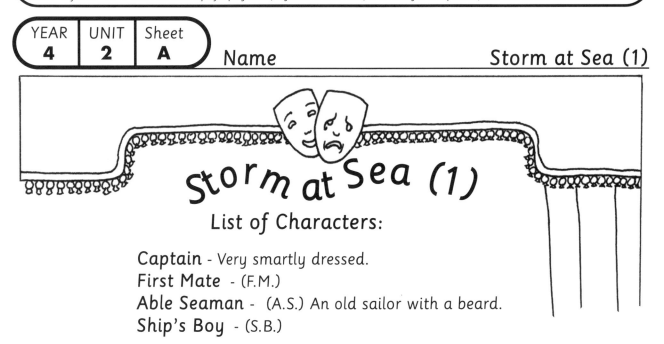

Storm at Sea (1)

List of Characters:

Captain - Very smartly dressed.
First Mate - (F.M.)
Able Seaman - (A.S.) An old sailor with a beard.
Ship's Boy - (S.B.)

SCENE ONE

On board a wooden sailing ship. There are barrels, ropes and wooden cases on the stage to give the impression of the deck of the ship. F.M. is standing at the ship's wheel. Captain is behind him to the right. Both are facing the audience. S.B. is sitting on a barrel at one side of the stage, plaiting some ropes together. A.S. is sitting on a wooden case.

Captain: 'Tis a fine day Mr. Mate.

F.M.:   'Tis indeed, Sir. One of the finest we've seen in the twelve days we've been travelling.

A.S.:   There's a storm brewing.

Captain: The sea is a beautiful blue Mr. Mate.

F.M.:   'Tis indeed, Sir. The bluest we've seen in the twelve days we've been travelling.

A.S.:   There's a storm brewing.

Captain: The wind is set fair Mr. Mate.

F.M.:   'Tis indeed, Sir. One of the fairest we've had in the twelve days we've been travelling.

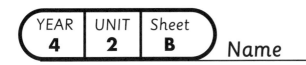

Name

Storm at Sea (1)

A.S.: (*crossly*) There's a storm brewing.

Captain: Able Seaman, raise an extra sail. With such a fair wind we'll make good distance today.

A.S.: Aye, aye, Captain but there's a storm brewing, you mark my words. Boy, help me raise this sail.

S.B.: Aye, aye, Sir.

Able Seaman and Ship's Boy haul on ropes to raise a sail.

Captain: There. Can you feel the difference? Can you see the difference?

F.M.: Aye, aye, Captain. Our speed is much better now.

A.S.: Aye, I can feel the difference, but we'll feel it more soon because there's a storm brewing.

S.B.: I'm scared.

A.S.: (*to S.B.*) Do you see that dark cloud in the sky?

S.B.: Yes.

A.S.: That's a storm brewing.

S.B.: I'm very scared.

A.S.: Do you see the white tops to those waves?

S.B.: I'm very, very scared.

All sway from side to side to indicate rough seas.

F.M.: The sea is becoming rough, Sir.

Captain: Nonsense. Haul up another sail, Able Seaman.

A.S.: But the storm's a-chasing us, Sir.

Captain: Nonsense. Do you argue with me? I am your Captain.

A.S.: No, Sir. I mean, yes, Sir. Boy help me raise this sail.

S.B.: Aye, aye, Sir.

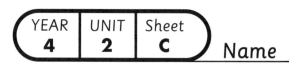
Able Seaman and Ship's Boy haul on ropes to raise a sail. Sound effects of heavy rain. All sway and stagger about as though struggling to stay on board.

S.B.:   (*sobbing loudly*) It's raining. The storm has reached us. I'm extremely scared!

Captain: (*shouting above the noise of the storm*) The storm has reached us! Just as I said it would!

F.M.:   You did indeed Sir.

All stagger about, clutching onto each other, the ship's wheel, the rails. They knock over barrels to give the impression that the barrels have tipped over in the storm. Ship's Boy suddenly leaps sideways as though washed overboard.

S.B.:   Help, I'm overboard! Help me!

Able Seaman rushes to the side of the ship and throws a rope towards the Ship's Boy. Ship's Boy tries to catch it but misses. Able Seaman tries again. Captain and First Mate simply cling to each other uselessly.

S.B.:   (*voice fading as he drifts away*) Help!
(*Exit, stage left.*)

A.S.:   He's lost!

Captain: But we are safe. The storm is fading.

A.S.:   But what about the boy?

Captain: You should have saved him. When we reach land you will be imprisoned for incompetence.

SCENE TWO

An empty stage. Ship's Boy is crawling as though reaching dry land from the sea. He looks exhausted.

S.B.:   Land! Land! I am safe.

He slowly sits up, then stands.

S.B.:   I hope that the ship returns safely to shore so that everyone knows how bravely the Able Seaman tried to rescue me and how useless the Captain and First Mate were.

What happens next? Will the Able Seaman be imprisoned or will he be praised for trying to save the Ship's Boy? You could write the next scene of the play. Remember to give stage directions as well as the script. You may need to introduce some new characters. Perhaps the scene could be set in a courtroom. Use the frame below and continue on the back of the sheet.

This unit addresses the Literacy Strategy:
Term 1 objective   1: to investigate how settings and characters are built up from small details, and how the reader responds to them.
Term 1 objective   2: to identify the main characteristics of the key characters, drawing on the text to justify views, and using the information to predict actions.
Term 1 objective   5: to prepare, read and perform playscripts; compare organisation of scripts with stories - how are settings indicated, story lines made clear?

YEAR **4** UNIT **3** Sheet **A**   **Name**   Storm at Sea (2)

Storm at Sea (2)

Reread the playscript in the unit Storm at Sea (1)

In the chest below are some adjectives that could be used to describe the four characters. Choose some adjectives for each person. Some adjectives could be used for more than one person. You could also think of more adjectives of your own. Explain to a friend why you have chosen the adjectives for each person.

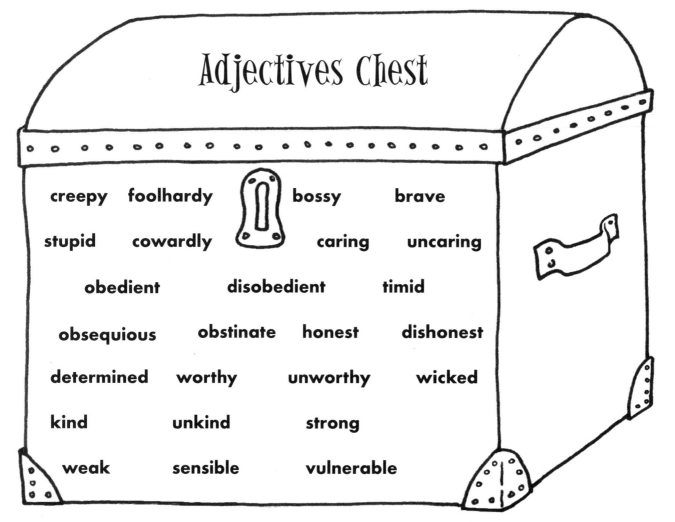

Adjectives Chest

creepy   foolhardy   bossy   brave

stupid   cowardly   caring   uncaring

obedient   disobedient   timid

obsequious   obstinate   honest   dishonest

determined   worthy   unworthy   wicked

kind   unkind   strong

weak   sensible   vulnerable

Captain

What do <u>you</u> think of the Captain?

Adjectives that could be used.

First Mate

What do <u>you</u> think of the First Mate?

Adjectives.

Able Seaman

What do <u>you</u> think of the Able Seaman?

Adjectives.

Ship's Boy

What do <u>you</u> think of the Ship's Boy?

Adjectives.

Here is part of the 'Storm at Sea' story again.

This time it is not written as a play script.

The ship was sailing well before the wind, its timbers hardly creaking and its sails hardly flapping so smooth was its ride on the clear blue sea.

All four members of the crew were enjoying the sunshine on the deck. The First Mate was in control of the ship's wheel, the Captain looking on.

" 'Tis a fine day, Mr Mate," said the Captain, with a contented smile on his face.

" 'Tis indeed, Sir. One of the finest we've had in the twelve days we've been travelling," replied the First Mate. He had a habit of always agreeing with the Captain, whether he was right or wrong.

But the Able Seaman thought differently. "There's a storm brewing," he said.

"The sea is a beautiful blue Mr. Mate," remarked the Captain, ignoring the Able Seaman.

" 'Tis indeed, Sir. The bluest we've seen in the twelve days we've been travelling."

1.   Compare this passage of prose to the play script. Discuss with a friend the similarities and the differences between the two pieces of writing.

2.   Now continue to rewrite the story as prose using the writing frame.

This unit addresses the Literacy Strategy:
Term 1 objective   1: to investigate how story settings and characters are built up from small details, and how the reader responds to them.
Term 1 objective   2: to identify the main characteristics of the key characters, drawing on the text to justify views, and using the information to predict actions.
Term 3 objective   3: to understand how paragraphs or chapters are used to collect, order and build up ideas.

| YEAR 4 | UNIT 4 | Sheet A |

Name

Characters

A Christmas Carol
by Charles Dickens (1812-1870)

Oh! But he was a tight-fisted hand at the grindstone, Scrooge! A squeezing, wrenching, grasping, scraping, clutching, covetous old sinner! Hard and sharp as flint, from which no steel had ever struck out generous fire; secret, and self-contained, and solitary as an oyster. The cold within him froze his old features, nipped his pointed nose, shrivelled his cheek, stiffened his gait; made his eyes red, his thin lips blue; and spoke out shrewdly in his grating voice. A frosty rime was on his head, and on his eyebrows, and his wiry chin. He carried his own low temperature always about with him; he iced his office in the dog-days; and didn't thaw it one degree at Christmas.

External heat and cold had little influence on Scrooge. No warmth could warm, no wintry weather chill him. No wind that blew was bitterer than he, no falling snow was more intent upon its purpose, no pelting rain less open to entreaty. Foul weather didn't know where to have him. The heaviest rain, and snow, and hail, and sleet, could boast of the advantage over him in only one respect. They often came down handsomely, and Scrooge never did.

Nobody ever stopped him in the street to say, with gladsome looks, "My dear Scrooge, how are you? When will you come to see me?" No beggars implored him to bestow a trifle, no children asked him what it was o'clock, no man or woman ever once in all his life inquired the way to such and such a place, of Scrooge. Even the blindmen's dogs appeared to know him; and when they saw him coming on, would tug their owners into door-ways and up courts; and then would wag their tails as though they said, "No eye at all is better than an evil eye, dark master!"

Robin Hood

by Henry Gilbert

A man stood close by the path, behind a tree, and looked out into the glade. He was dressed in a tunic made of rough green cloth, open at the top, and showing a bronzed neck. Round his waist was a broad leathern girdle in which were stuck at one place a dagger, and at the other side three long arrows. Soft breeches of soft leather covered his thighs, below which he wore hosen of green wool, which reached to his feet. The latter were encased in shoes of stout pig's leather.

His head of dark brown curls was covered by a velvet cap, at the side of which was stuck a short feather, pulled from the wing of a plover. His face, bronzed for a ruddy tan by wind and weather, was open and frank, his eye shone like a wild bird's, and was as fearless and as noble. Great of limb was he, and seemingly of a strength beyond his age, which was about twenty-five years. In one hand he carried a long-bow, while the other rested on the smooth bole of the beech before him.

Name the famous author who wrote 'A Christmas Carol'.

_____

Name the characters described in the two extracts.

_____   _____

Write four of the adjectives used to describe Scrooge in the second sentence of the extract.

_____   _____

_____   _____

Explain the meaning of the following phrase 'No children ever asked him what it was o'clock'.

_____

_____

_____

Write the phrase from the Robin Hood text that tells the reader he was a tall man.

_____

_____

How old was Robin Hood?

_____

_____

Explain the following words. You may need a dictionary to help you.

From the Robin Hood extract:

plover   _____

beech   _____

From the Christmas Carol extract:

gladsome   _____

solitary   _____

On the back draw a detailed picture of each of the two characters, based on the information in the extracts.

What kind of person do you think Mr Scrooge was? Give reasons for your answer.

_____

_____

_____

Write one sentence about each of the three paragraphs in the Scrooge extract. The sentences should describe the key points of the paragraphs.

1. _____

_____

2. _____

_____

3. _____

_____

What kind of person do you think Robin Hood was? Give reasons for your answer.

_____

_____

_____

Write the phrase from the Robin Hood text that tells us he has a suntan from spending time outdoors.

_____

_____

From the text would you think Scrooge was younger or older than Robin Hood? Give reasons for your answer.

_____

_____

_____

Explain the phrase 'No beggars implored him to bestow a trifle'.

_____

_____

This unit addresses the Literacy Strategy:
Term 1 objective   7: compare and contrast poems on similar themes, particularly their form and language, discussing personal responses and preferences.
Term 2 objective   7: to identify different patterns of rhyme and verse in poetry, e.g. choruses, rhyming couplets, alternate line rhymes and to read these aloud effectively.

YEAR 4 **UNIT 5** **Sheet A**   **Name**   **Moral Poems**

On these pages are two poems by different poets.

Each poem has a lesson to learn, and a similar ending.

Matilda Who Told Lies, and Was Burned to Death.
(Hilaire Belloc 1870-1953)

Matilda told such Dreadful Lies,
It made one Gasp and Stretch one's Eyes;

Her Aunt, who, from her Earliest Youth,
Had kept a Strict Regard for Truth,
Attempted to Believe Matilda:
The effort very nearly killed her,
And would have done so, had not She
Discovered this Infirmity.

For once, towards the Close of Day,
Matilda, growing tired of play,
And finding she was left alone,
Went tiptoe to the Telephone
And summoned the Immediate Aid
Of London's Noble Fire-Brigade.

Within an hour the Gallant Band
Were pouring in on every hand,
From Putney,
Hackney Downs
and Bow.
With Courage
high and Hearts
a-glow,
They galloped, roaring
through the Town,
'Matilda's House is
Burning Down!'

Inspired by British
Cheers and Loud
Proceeding from the
Frenzied Crowd,

They ran their ladders through a score
Of windows on the Ball Room Floor;
And took Peculiar Pains to Souse
The Pictures up and down the House,
Until Matilda's Aunt succeeded
In showing them they were not needed;
And even then she had to pay
To get the men to go away!

It happened that a few Weeks later
Her Aunt was off to the Theatre
To see that Interesting Play
The Second Mrs Tanqueray.

She had refused to take her Niece
To hear this Entertaining Piece:
A Deprivation Just and Wise
To Punish her for Telling Lies.

That Night a Fire did break out -
You should have heard Matilda Shout!
You should have heard her Scream and Bawl,
And throw the window up and call
To People passing in the Street -
(The rapidly increasing Heat
Encouraging her to obtain
Their confidence) - but all in vain!

For every time She shouted 'Fire!'
They only answered 'Little Liar!'
And therefore when her Aunt returned,
Matilda, and the House, were Burned.

Reprinted by permission of PFD on behalf of: The Estate of Hilaire Belloc.   © The Estate of Hilaire Belloc: as printed in the original volume.

Dreadful Story About Harriet and the Matches

(Heinrich Hoffmann 1809-1874)

It almost makes me cry to tell
What foolish Harriet befell.
Mamma and Nurse went out one day
And left her alone at play;
Now, on the table close at hand,
A box of matches chanc'd to stand;
And kind Mamma and Nurse had told her
That, if she touch'd them, they should scold her.
But Harriet said: "O, what a pity!
For, when they burn, it is so pretty;
They crackle so, and spit, and flame;
Mamma, too, often does the same."

The pussy-cats heard this,
And they began to hiss,
And stretch their claws
And raise their paws;
"Me-ow," they said, "me-ow, me-o,
You'll burn to death, if you do so."

But Harriet would not take advice,
She lit a match, it was so nice!
It crackled so, it burn'd so clear, -
Exactly like the picture here.
She jump'd for joy and ran about
And was too pleas'd to put it out.

The pussy-cats saw this
And said: "Oh, naughty, naughty Miss!"
And stretch'd their claws and raised their paws:
"'Tis very, very wrong, you know,
Me-ow, me-o, me-ow, me-o,
You will be burnt, if you do so."

And see! Oh! what a dreadful thing!
The fire has caught her apron-string;
Her apron burns, her arms, her hair;
She burns all over, everywhere.

Then how they pussy-cats did mew,
What else, poor pussies, could they do?

They scream'd for help, 'twas all in vain!
So then, they said: "We'll scream again;
Make haste, make haste, me-ow, me-o,
She'll burn to death, we told her so."

So she was burnt, with all her clothes,
And arms, and hands, and eyes, and nose;
Till she had nothing more to lose
Except her little scarlet shoes;
And nothing else but these was found
Among her ashes on the ground.

And when the good cats sat beside
The smoking ashes, how they cried!
"Me-ow, me-oo, me-ow, me-oo,
What will Mamma and Nursy do?"
Their tears ran down their cheeks so fast;
They made a little pond at last.

1.   These two poems have a similar theme. Ring the sentence that correctly describes the theme of the poems.

Not following rules can have tragic results.

Fire is dangerous.

Little girls are naughty.

2.   Name the poet who wrote 'Dreadful Story About Harriet and the Matches'.

_____

3.   Who wrote the poem about 'Matilda'?

_____

4.   What is the same about the ending of each poem?

_____

5.   What word is used to rhyme with <u>score</u> in one of the poems?

_____

6.   Which character wore red shoes?

_____

7.   Who's aunt went to the theatre?

_____

8.   What was the title of the play she went to see?

_____

9.   Which of the poems do you prefer? Give reasons for your choice.

_____

_____

_____

_____

_____

10. On the back of the sheet write 8 lines of the poem you preferred. Use your best writing and illustrate the section of the poem you have written.

11.   Which of the following describes the structure of both poems?

      4 line verses   **alliteration**   **rhyming couplets**

12.   In both poems how many syllables per line help create the rhythm?   _____

13.   Write the two lines from one of the poems, that refer to an illustration.

      _____

      _____

14.   What is referred to in one of the poems as the 'gallant band'?

      _____

      _____

15.   How does the reader know that Matilda's tragedy happened in London?

      _____

      _____

16.   Name three areas of London referred to in that poem.

      _____

17.   Which of the following words means the same as souse (Matilda - line 25)?
      Ring the correct answer.

            ruin   **drench**   **clean**   **take**

18.   At the beginning of the 'Harriet' poem, what does the line
      '*What foolish Harriet befell*', mean?

      _____

      _____

19.   In the same poem, what is meant by
      '*They crackle so, and spit, and flame;*
      Mama, too, often does the same'.

      _____

      _____

20.   On the back of the sheet write a poem of your own in which not following safety
      rules leads to problems. (Perhaps you have learned the hard way that rules are
      there to keep you safe.)

YEAR **4** | UNIT **6** | Sheet **A**   *Name*   The Railway Children

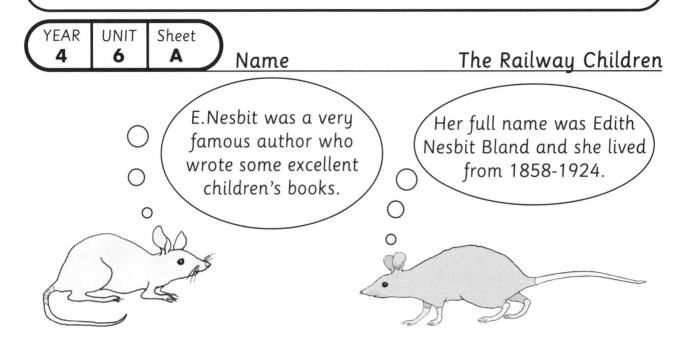

E.Nesbit was a very famous author who wrote some excellent children's books.

Her full name was Edith Nesbit Bland and she lived from 1858-1924.

This extract is taken from the first chapter of the book 'The Railway Children'. This text begins with the three children and their mother travelling by train to a new house.

At first they enjoyed looking out of the window, but when it grew dark they grew sleepier and sleepier, and no one knew how long they had been in the train when they were roused by Mother's shaking them gently and saying - 'Wake up, dears. We're here.'

They woke up, cold and melancholy, and stood shivering on the draughty platform while the luggage was taken out of the train. Then the engine, puffing and blowing, set to work again, and dragged the train away. The children watched the tail-lights of the guard's van disappear into the darkness.

This was the first train the children saw on the railway which was, in time, to become so very dear to them. They did not guess then how they would grow to love the railway, and how soon it would become the centre of their new life, nor what wonders and changes it would bring them. They only shivered and sneezed and hoped the walk to the new house would not be long. Peter's nose was colder than he ever remembered it to have been before. Roberta's hat was crooked, and the elastic seemed tighter than usual. Phyllis's shoelaces had come undone.

'Come,' said Mother, 'we've got to walk. There aren't any cabs here.'

The walk was dark and muddy. The children stumbled a little on the rough road, and once Phyllis absently fell into a puddle, and was picked up damp and unhappy. There were no gas-lamps on the road, and the road was uphill. The cart went at a foot's pace, and they followed the gritty crunch of its wheels. As their eyes got used to the darkness, they could see the mound of boxes swaying dimly in front of them.

A long gate had to be opened for the cart to pass through, and after that the road seemed to go across fields - and now it went downhill. Presently a great dark lumpish thing showed over to the right.

'There's the house,' said Mother. 'I wonder why she's shut the shutters.'

'Who's she?' asked Roberta.

'The woman I engaged to clean the place, and put the furniture straight and get supper.'

There was a low wall and trees inside.

'That's the garden,' said Mother.

'It looks more like a dripping-pan full of black cabbages,' said Peter.

The cart went on along by the garden wall, and round to the back of the house, and here it clattered into a cobblestoned yard and stopped at the back door. There was no light in any of the windows.

Everyone hammered at the door, but no one came.

The man who drove the cart said he expected Mrs Viney had gone home.

'You see your train was late.' said he.

'But she's got the key,' said Mother. 'What are we to do?'

'Oh, she'll have left that under the doorstep,' said the cart man; 'folks do here-abouts.' He took the lantern off his cart and stooped.

'Ay, here it is, right enough,' said he.

He unlocked the door and went in and set his lantern on the table.

'Got e're a candle?' said he.

'I don't know where anything is.' Mother spoke rather less cheerfully than usual.

He struck a match. There was a candle on the table, and he lighted it. By its thin little glimmer the children saw a large bare kitchen with a stone floor. There were no curtains, no hearthrug. The kitchen table from home stood in the middle of the room. The chairs were in one corner, and the pots, pans, brooms, and crockery in another. There was no fire, and the black grate showed cold, dead ashes.

As the cart man turned to go out after he had brought in the boxes, there was a rustling, scampering sound that seemed to come from inside the walls of the house.

'Oh, what's that?' cried the girls.

'It's only rats,' said the cart man. And he went away and shut the door, and the sudden draught of it blew out the candle.

'Oh dear,' said Phyllis, 'I wish we hadn't come!' and she knocked a chair over.

'Only the rats!' said Peter, in the dark.

If you enjoyed the extract you might want to read the whole book. It is a very exciting story. Some other books by E.Nesbit that you might enjoy, include-
'Five Children and It', 'The Phoenix and the Carpet', 'The Wouldbegoods', 'The Story of the Amulet' and 'The Story of the Treasure Seekers'.

Name   The Railway Children

❦ Who wrote the book 'The Railway Children'?

_____

❦ Name three other books by the same author.

_____

_____

_____

❦ What were the names of the three children in the story?

_____

❦ How did the children and their mother get from the station to their new home?

_____

_____

_____

❦ Find, and write, the sentence that tells you that the children were not looking forward to the walk.

_____

_____

❦ How does Peter describe the look of the garden?

_____

_____

❦ Write the phrase that tells us how slowly the cart travelled.

_____

_____

❦ What does the cart man say is making the scampering sounds in the walls of the house.

_____

_____

❦ On the back of the sheet make a list of all the things in the extract that show the story is set in the past. Share your list with a friend.

🐛 Write a sentence from the text that leads the reader to understand that the train the children arrived on was powered by a steam engine.

_____

_____

🐛 Which of the following words is nearest in meaning to 'melancholy'
Ring the correct answer.

mellow   **minute**   **misty**   **miserable**

🐛 The children walked from the station to their new home. What was the cart used for?

_____

_____

🐛 Name the three sorts of lighting referred to in the text.

_____

_____

🐛 What adjective is used to describe the station platform.   _____

🐛 Mother says she 'engaged a woman to clean the place'. Which of the following words could correctly replace the word engaged. Ring the correct answer.

asked   **employed**   **offered**   **needed**

🐛 What made it possible for the children to follow the cart when it couldn't be seen in the darkness?

_____

_____

🐛 How is the light from the candle on the kitchen table described in the text?

_____

_____

🐛 What was in the fire grate?

_____

_____

🐛 On the back, present the story as a comic strip. Include detailed pictures showing that the story is set in the past. Include dialogue between the characters in each picture. Use the space below each picture to write the story in your own words. Make it as interesting as you can.

This unit addresses the Literacy Strategy:
Term 1 objective   16: to identify different types of text, e.g. their content, structure, vocabulary, style, lay-out and purpose.
Term 1 objective   17: to identify features of non-fiction texts in print and IT, e.g. headings, lists, bullet points, captions which support the reader
in gaining information efficiently.

YEAR	UNIT	Sheet
4	7	A

Name _____   Information Leaflet

Look at the holiday cottage leaflet and answer the following questions.

1.   What is the purpose of the information?

☐   **To tell you how to get to St Malo.**

☐   **To advertise a holiday home in Brittany, France.**

☐   **To advertise beaches and water sports.**

2.   Read the following list of features found under the main title 'Enjoying a Holiday for All the Family In Our Perfect Holiday Home in the Heart of Chateauneuf, North Brittany, France'.

The house is well placed for visits to the old walled city of St Malo.

The house sleeps 6 people

Close to ferry port

Beautiful location

Dozens of secret sandy beaches

Now write a list of features that would attract children to come to your school.

① _____

_____

② _____

_____

③ _____

_____

④ _____

_____

The ideal route, if you are contemplating travelling with Brittany Ferries, is to use the Portsmouth to St Malo crossings as you will be just 15 minutes away from the holiday you've always been waiting for.

Directions From St Malo:

From St Malo follow signs for Chateauneuf along the N139. On entering the village the house will be found in the Rue du Chateau next to the church.

The minute you walk in to the cottage the holiday of your lifetime will be waiting for you! Have a really relaxing rest in a peaceful and tranquil environment.

6

5

The address of this truly magnificent cottage is:

Chez Nous
Rue du Chateau,
Chateauneuf,
Ille et Vilaine,
Brittany,
France

For further details please contact
Mr & Mrs Grant on: 02934 993590.

Enjoy A Holiday For
All The Family In
Our Perfect Holiday
Home In The Heart
Of Chateauneuf -
North Brittany!
FRANCE

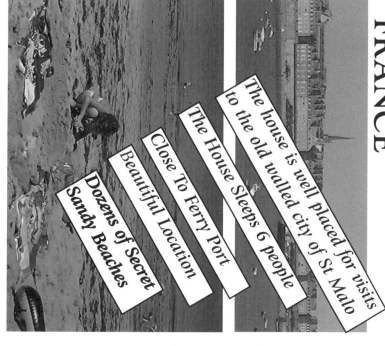

The house is well placed for visits to the old walled city of St Malo

The House Sleeps 6 people

Close To Ferry Port

Beautiful Location

Dozens of Secret Sandy Beaches

1

About the house

This magnificent holiday home in Chateauneuf, 10km from St Malo, is ideal for all the family. It can sleep up to 6 people and offers, on the ground floor, a kitchen, spacious lounge, dining area and shower room. There are two bedrooms and a bathroom on the first floor and an attractive attic room which looks out over the Chateau. It has a well fitted kitchen with a washing machine, drier, fridge, freezer and gas cooker.

If you don't like cooking, treat yourself to a meal out at a restaurant which serves local cuisine and seafood or if you are just looking for a snack visit a creperie. Brittany is well known for its delicious crepes and people often eat out.

Why not enhance your breakfast by a short walk to the boulangerie which offers a range of croissants, breads and pastries freshly baked?

2

We let our cottage out for the summer months only. Below is a table of the costs per week.

	April	May	June	July	Aug	Sept
Cost per week in £	£160	£180	£200	£220	£240	£140
Cost per week in €	€240	€270	€300	€330	€360	€210

The old walled city of St Malo

The sea is there for all ages.

A beautiful Brittany beach.

4

Things to do & see

Dinan – Visit the fascinating medieval port of Dinan which offers fishing, boating and kayaking on a stunningly beautiful stretch of the River Rance. There are also dozens of shops selling crafts and fine art work to suite all tastes.

St Malo – St Malo is one of the jewels of France. It has a lovely old walled town with good shops and restaurants and stunning views from the walk around the walls.

Mont St Michel – A visit to Mont St Michel, one of France's largest tourist attractions, is a must with its fortress-like island of churches and spires rising out of the bay.

Cancale – Cancale is a picturesque fishing port famous for its oyster beds. Wander round the streets studying the menus listed outside the many welcoming restaurants and then treat yourself to a meal of local fresh water fish and a delectable crepe for dessert.

Local Beaches – The Brittany coastline has many safe sandy beaches offering a variety of water sports or for just boating and our previous guests have sampled them all! There is a book in the house with their comments and suggestions for the perfect day out at the beach. Please add yours!

3

3. Under the heading 'About the house', find two words that are from the French language.

   1. [   ]   **2.** [   ]

4. Under the heading 'Things to do and see' find out what Cancale is famous for.

   _____

   _____

5. In Dinan what sports might you do on the River Rance?

   _____

   _____

6. How much would you expect to pay for the holiday home for a week in July? Give your answer in pounds and in euros.

   _____

   _____

7. How much would you expect to pay for the holiday home for 2 weeks in June? Give your answer in pounds and in euros.

   _____

   _____

8. Does this brochure make you want to go to France on holiday? Explain your answer giving reasons why you would like to go to the place described or why you would not like to go there.

   _____

   _____

   _____

   _____

   _____

   _____

   _____

   _____

9. Design a brochure to advertise your school to new pupils. Make use of headings, different text sizes, illustrations, clear vocabulary, bullet points, lists and paragraphs.

This unit addresses the Literacy Strategy:
Term 1 objective 20: to identify the main features of newspapers, including layout, range of information, voice, level of formality; organisation of articles, advertisements and headlines.
Term 1 objective 21: predict newspaper stories from the evidence of headlines.

YEAR	UNIT	Sheet
4	8	A

Name   Headlines

1. Predict the story that might appear under each of these headlines. Briefly discuss the possibilities with a partner.

LOCAL BOY WINS
BALLOON RACE
...BY FAR.

BRAVE TEACHER
WINS AWARD

CUP FINAL-
WIN FOR
REDS.

Bomb Scare at School
Building Site

FISH DIE IN POLLUTION ALERT

2. Read the following three newspaper articles and select an appropriate headline for each one from the selection on the first sheet. Write your choice in the space above each one.

Mr James Palmer was given the Queen's Award for Bravery today following the rescue of three people from a cliff ledge last summer.

Mr Palmer, who teaches at Wood Lane School in Somerset, was on a school trip with 26 youngsters and four other adults.

They were walking along the cliff path when cries for help were heard from below. Mr Palmer looked over the edge of the cliff and saw three people on a very narrow ledge; one was lying unconscious on his back and two others were shouting for help.

"I could see they were only teenagers and that they were terrified," said Mr Palmer. "I did what anyone else would have done and climbed down with a rope support to see what I could do to help until the emergency services arrived."

Mr Palmer kept Steven King, aged 18, alive by mouth to mouth resuscitation.

Steven said, "If it wasn't for James I would not be here today. I owe my life to him. I won't be going near the cliffs again."

Farm waste which polluted a stream flowing into the River Bow has killed hundreds of fish. Children spotted the fish flapping about in the water and lying on the bank gasping for air. Kirsty Snow, one of the children, said the water looked black.

"We have been doing some work on pollution at school," said Kirsty. "I knew the fish would die because they wouldn't have enough oxygen in the water." The children followed the pollution back to the farm which was allowing slurry to go into the stream. The police have been informed.

_____
_____

When young Santosh Kumar went to her school fete in July she had no idea she would make the headlines.

Santosh paid £1 for her name to go on a tag tied to a helium filled balloon. At 3pm 200 balloons were released into the sky. The tag returned to school by 1st September from the furthest distance away would win a hot-air balloon flight.

Santosh's tag was returned from Stuttgart in Germany.

Santosh is now looking forward to her balloon flight.

"But I don't think we'll get as far as Germany!" said Santosh.

3. Look through at least two different newspapers.

    Look at   - the layout
               - the headlines
               - the range of information other than news
               - advertisements

    Make a list of four types of information you may find in a newspaper, other than news.

    1. _____   **3.** _____

    2. _____   **4.** _____

4. Which two of the following sentences comes from a newspaper article?

    a.   **Holiday-makers spoke yesterday of terror after a fire broke out at a hotel.**

    b.   **The sun shone down in rays between the cotton wool clouds.**

    c.   **He trudged slowly, head down, along the muddy streets looking for a place to rest.**

    d.   **Two men were arrested for stealing a motorbike worth £2000.**

5. Make up some newspaper headlines of your own. Remember, they should be short and they should make the reader want to read on to find out more.

    _____

    _____

    _____

    _____

6. Now choose one of your headlines to develop into a newspaper style story.

    Write a rough draft of your story first, then check it for spelling mistakes and to see if it makes sense. Decide whether it is interesting enough and whether it is written in the style of a newspaper.

    When you are happy with your story, write it out in columns so that it looks like a newspaper story. You may like to use the computer.

YEAR 4	UNIT 9	Sheet A	Name

Tim's Cooking Exploits

Read Tim's account of his cookery exploits.

I put the cooker on then I got the stuff ready. I got some eggs out of the fridge. And butter. Mum got the caster sugar and flour for me because I couldn't reach. And the baking powder. The paper cups were all stuck together and I put two by mistake in some of the holes in the tin thing. Mum says it's called a patty tin. I put all the stuff into a big bowl then I put the mixer in and switched it on and the egg splattered onto the wall. Mum said I should mix the stuff for two minutes but I did it for ages then I scooped mixture into all the paper cases. I put the cake tin into the oven very carefully because I hate getting burnt. Then I watched television until Mum shouted at me because the cakes might get burnt. I took them out of the oven. I had to wear thick gloves because I hate getting burnt. They looked good.

How good is
Tim's account?

Is it clear?

1. What was Tim making?

_____

_____

2. In what part of the extract do you find out what he was making?

_____

_____

3. Do we know how many eggs Tim used?   _____

4. What other ingredients did he use?

_____

_____

5. What does Tim hate?

_____

6. How could Tim have improved his account?

_____

_____

_____

Now read the recipe
that Tim followed.

Simply Super Sponges

Ingredients:

2 eggs

100 grams of self-raising flour

100 grams of caster sugar

100 grams of butter (at room temperature)

1 level teaspoon of baking powder

Method:

Pre-heat oven to 180°C.
Place paper cases in a patty tin.
Put all your ingredients into a mixing bowl.
Use an electric mixer to beat ingredients together
for about 2 minutes.
Put a heaped teaspoon of the mixture into each
paper case.
Carefully place the patty tin into the oven.
Leave for fifteen minutes or until golden brown.
Carefully remove from oven.
Leave to cool.

Take care when cooking. The oven is hot!

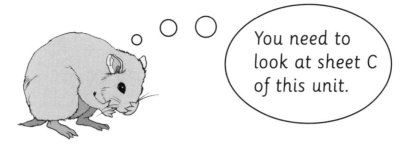

You need to
look at sheet C
of this unit.

1. What is the special name for instructions on how to cook something? You will
need these letters:

e	e	i	p	r	c	_____

2. The words in the title all begin with the letter 's'. What is the special name for
several words all starting with the same letter being used deliberately? You
will need these letters:

a	a	e	i	i	o	l	l	n	r	t	t

_____

3. As in Tim's account, we can see what ingredients are needed. In what way is
this information presented differently to the way Tim presented it?

_____

_____

_____

4. You have read a set of instructions for making cakes. Now write some
instructions of your own. Think of something you do every day, such as opening
a door, and write detailed instructions. Use the back of the sheet if you need to.

_____

_____

_____

_____

_____

_____

_____

_____

_____

This unit addresses the Literacy Strategy:
Term 1 objective 22: to identify features of instructional texts including: - noting the intended outcome at the beginning; clearly set out sequential stages; language of commands, e.g. imperative verbs.

YEAR **4** | UNIT **10** | Sheet **A** | **Name** | **Instructional Texts**

Instructional Texts

Look at the following sets of instructions.

VEGETABLE STEW

Ingredients:

Serves 4/6 people

1 large onion
small swede (or $\frac{1}{2}$ large swede)
4 carrots
2 leeks
red pepper
2 courgettes
1 tin chopped tomatoes
salt and pepper
teaspoon dried mixed herbs
tablespoon olive oil

you will also need a large saucepan and lid

1. Peel and slice onion thinly.

2. Cut red pepper in half and remove all seeds, dice into small pieces.

3. Prepare and slice the carrot, swede, leeks and courgettes.

4. Gently fry the onions in the olive oil for 3 minutes.

5. Add the other prepared vegetables and fry for 1 minute.

6. Add the tin of chopped tomatoes, herbs and salt and pepper to taste.

7. Put on lid and simmer on a low heat for 20 minutes or until the vegetables are tender.

8. Serve in a bowl with crusty bread or a baked potato.

OUT OF SCHOOL CLUBS FOR YEAR 4

☆ Choose the clubs you would like to go to this term from the list below.

☆ You may attend as many as you wish providing spaces are available.

☆ Once you are given a place in a club you are expected to continue for the whole term.

☆ Why not have a go at something new? 'Skipping Club' and 'Graphic Design' are both offered for the first time, so will be new for everyone.

☆ Ask your parent or carer to sign the form before returning it to the School Office by Friday 12th September.

	Name of Club	Time	Place	Teacher
☐	Archery	Mon 3 → 4pm	School Field	Mrs Flight
☐	Basketball	Mon 3 → 4pm	Hall	Mr Long
☐	Chess Club	Tues 3 → 4pm	Class 3	Miss Knight
☐	Computer Club	Thurs 3 → 4pm	Computer Suite	Mrs Mack
☐	Choir	Wed 3 → 4pm	Hall	Mr Singer
☐	Football	Tues 3 → 4pm	School Field	Mrs Green
☐	Hockey	Wed 3 → 4pm	School Field	Mr Pitch
☐	Graphic Design	Thurs 3 → 4pm	Computer Suite	Mr Patten
☐	Line Dancing	Thurs 3 → 4pm	Hall	Mr Time
☐	Skipping	Tues 3 → 4pm	Hall	Mrs Rope

Child's Name...

I agree to my child attending the clubs indicated above and will be able to collect him or her at the end of the session.

Parent/Carer signature...

Instructional Texts

1. In instructional texts you are likely to find:

☐ **long descriptions**   ☐ **rhyming words**

☐ **clear lists**   ☐ **statements set out in a sequence or logical order**

Tick two of the boxes.

2. a) Look at the recipe for Vegetable Stew. How long should you fry the onion for?

_____

b) Name the six fresh vegetables used in the recipe.

1. _____   **4.** _____

2. _____   **5.** _____

3. _____   **6.** _____

3. How long should the stew be simmered for?

_____

4. What does the word 'simmer' mean?

simmer: _____

_____

_____

_____

5. Write a recipe for making a Fresh Fruit Salad.

Use your favourite fruits and illustrate with pictures or diagrams.

Name _____   Instructional Texts

Read the information about 'Out of School Clubs'.

1. The list of clubs should be in alphabetical order but there are two errors.
    Rewrite the list in the correct alphabetical order.

1. _____   6. _____

2. _____   7. _____

3. _____   8. _____

4. _____   9. _____

5. _____   10. _____

2. A mistake has been made with the information about the Graphic Design Club
    and the Computer Club. Can you see what it might be?

    _____

    _____

    _____

3. What clubs are available on Mondays?

    _____   _____

4. Write a simple timetable for the use of the Hall between 3 and 4 pm on
    weekdays. The first one has been done for you.

Out of School Clubs
Hall Timetable

Day	Club
Monday	Basketball

5. Why does a parent or carer have to sign the form?

    _____

    _____

    _____

This unit addresses the Literacy Strategy:
Term 1 objective 22: to identify features of instructional texts including: noting the intended outcome at the beginning; listing materials or ingredients; clearly set out sequential stages; language of commands, e.g. imperative verbs.

Making a Pop-up Greetings Card

Follow the instructions to make a pop-up card. Change the decoration and greeting to use this type of card for a variety of occasions.

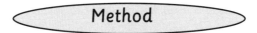

Materials

- ➤ 2 sheets of A4 paper or thin card.
- ➤ Glue suitable for sticking paper or card.
- ➤ Pencil.
- ➤ Ruler.
- ➤ Scissors.
- ➤ Art materials for decorating your card.

Method

1. Fold each piece of paper into half as shown below.

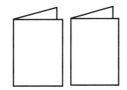

2. Mark <u>one</u> piece of paper with a dot half way along the folded edge. This piece of paper will be the inner layer of your finished card.

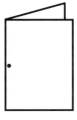

3. Draw 2 lines, each 3 centimetres long, 2 centimetres each side of the dot. (Your lines will be 4cm apart.)

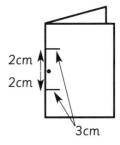

2cm

2cm

3cm

4. Cut along each of your lines.

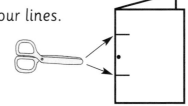

5. Draw a line to join the ends of the two cuts.

6.   Press a crease along the line you have drawn.

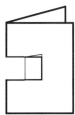

7.   Open up your paper (or card) and push the fold the other way. Close the card to make another firm crease.

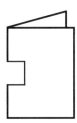 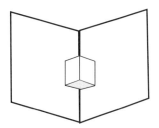

8.   Use your art materials to draw, cut out and colour a picture or symbol of your choice.

9.   Glue this to your pop-up card centre.

Have a 'COOL'
birthday

10.   Write a greeting in your card.

11.   Take the second piece of A4 paper and glue it to outside of the inner layer.

12.   Decorate the outer layer of your card.

IDEAS

💡   Stick your picture so the card opens vertically.

💡   Stick pictures on both sides of your pop-up centre.

💡   Experiment with other pop-up shapes that you can decorate.

Pop-up
Greetings Card

1. Ring the phrase that means the same as <u>materials</u>.

   things to do   **things you need to use**   **scissors and pen**

2. Ring the phrase that means the same as <u>method</u>.

   what to wear   **what to do**   **paper folding**

3. Why are diagrams included with the instructions?

   _____

   _____

   _____

4. How many numbered instructions are there? _____

5. Why are the instructions numbered?

   _____

   _____

   _____

6. What does instruction number 9 tell you to do?

   _____

   _____

   _____

7. Name three occasions on which people often send greetings cards.

   _____   _____

   _____

8. Design a pop-up centre to a card you would like to make.

Perhaps you could follow the instructions to make a card.

YEAR	UNIT	Sheet
4	**11**	**D**

Name

Pop-up
Greetings Card

9. On the lines below, write the first word from each of the twelve numbered instructions.

_____   _____   _____

_____   _____   _____

_____   _____   _____

_____   _____   _____

10. What do all the words you have written have in common?

_____

_____

11. Why do you think instructions usually begin with verbs?

_____

_____

_____

12. Why are the materials marked with bullet points rather than numbers?

_____

_____

13. If you read the instructions again you will see there are very few adjectives (describing words). Why do you think that is?

_____

_____

_____

Perhaps you could try making your own pop-up design.

This unit addresses the Literacy Strategy:
Term 2 objective   2: to understand how settings influence events and incidents in stories and how they effect characters' behaviour.
Term 2 objective   4: to understand how the use of expressive and descriptive language can e.g. create moods, arouse expectations, build
tension, describe attitudes or emotions.

| YEAR 4 | UNIT 12 | Sheet A | Name | Tirok's Voyage(1) |

Tirok's Voyage to Fame (part 1)

Chapter One

Leaving Gatteoc

Tirok was ten years old, earth years that is, and had celebrated his birthday the previous week. For his age he was average height, average weight, average ability. In fact, everything about him seemed to be rather average and that was how he thought of himself. He was a popular boy, being friendly and quite courageous. Not the sort of courage that was noisy and boisterous, but the sort that no one would know existed until it was needed. Indeed Tirok would need this quiet courage sooner than anyone could possibly have imagined.

The birthday celebration had been combined with a leaving party as Tirok was going home. At least he was heading to the planet his parents had always talked of as home. For the first ten years of his life he had been growing up very happily on a scientific survey. He was used to seeing three moons at night, and during the day a large and rather beautiful sun that bathed everything in a warm pale blue light. His friends came from a variety of planets, but like him they all felt at home on Gatteoc.

Six weeks, the journey home should take, passing through several galaxies. What would life be like when he got there? How strange would it be living on a planet inhabited almost entirely by humanoids? Unlike his parents Tirok didn't feel as if he was going home, he felt as if he were leaving home. When he thought about it too hard, it seemed to flood him with homesickness even before he left.

Tirok woke up early that morning. For a moment he thought it was just another ordinary day. Then he remembered. This was the day his parents had been so looking forward to: the day they were leaving to return to Earth. His stomach knotted, and he didn't feel like eating breakfast. Teeth were cleaned, travelling clothes were put on, the last few things were put into bags and the family were ready to go.

The inter-galaxy terminal of the travelport was a new experience for the young traveller, its massive halls a temporary home to the largest space vehicles that he had ever seen. Instead of the usual bronze shades of the local interplanetary runabouts, their craft was stunning colours that Tirok had never seen before and didn't have a word to adequately describe. The nearest he could get to it when later recounting his experiences, was, 'a sort of greenish, purplish, silvery colour that never quite stood still'.

Soon the three travellers were alerted that their ship was ready for them to board. Now Tirok was feeling very apprehensive. A niggling nervousness floated around his body. As they boarded he marvelled at the sheer size of the craft that was to be their home for the next six weeks.

He quickly discovered that there was a crew of over a hundred, and more than a thousand passengers, some from distant worlds that were unknown to him. There was a maze of corridors, with illuminated signs in the languages of many worlds. The shimmering silver walls and floating walkways were intimidating, yet at the same time rather exciting. They seemed to be announcing the onset of an adventure.

… However, no one could have foreseen the magnitude of this adventure. The events about to unfold would change Tirok's life forever.

To answer these questions just put a ring around the correct word.

1. Which word could have been used instead of <u>courageous</u>?

   noisy   **brave**   **cowardly**   **polite**

2. Which word could have been used instead of <u>variety</u>?

   far   **near**   **cluster**   **range**

3. Which word could have been used instead of <u>planet</u>?

   world   **moon**   **town**   **house**

4. Which word could have been used instead of <u>ordinary</u>?

   adventurous   **interesting**   **school**   **normal**

5. Which word could have been used instead of <u>massive</u>?

   miniature   **huge**   **high**   **long**

Write the answers to the following questions.

6. Write the phrase in the first paragraph, that tells you Tirok was well liked.

   _____

7. How is the colouring of the interplanetary runabout described?

   _____

8. Write the 12 letter word that tells you how Tirok
   felt when it was time to board the spacecraft. _____

9. Name the planet Tirok was leaving. _____

10. Name the planet he was travelling to. _____

11. Draw and colour what you think the inside of the spacecraft looked like. Read
    Sheet B carefully first so that you don't miss anything important.

12. Write the words from the text that give you the first indication that this is a
     science fiction story.

     _____

13. The word Gatteoc is an anagram of another word. Gatteoc was home to Tirok,
     the anagram of gatteoc would be a home for some people. Can you work out
     what the word is?

     _____

14. In the text , though we are told very little about Gatteoc, one sentence tells us
     that it is different from Earth. Write that sentence.

     _____

     _____

     _____

15. Write two <u>phrases</u> from the text that are used to describe how Tirok felt on
     <u>the day they left Gatteoc.</u>

     _____

     _____

     _____

16. How does the author ensure that the reader knows that on Gatteoc the
     inhabitants did not all resemble humans?

     _____

     _____

     _____

17. Which sentence in the text first tells the reader that Tirok will be the central
     character and hero of the story?

     _____

     _____

18. Write the word used by the author to describe the
     size and importance of the events that will take place._____

19. Write the sentence that the author uses to both describe the inside of the space
     craft and to build the atmosphere of forthcoming adventure.

     _____

     _____

     _____

Tirok's Voyage to Fame (part 2)

Chapter Two

New Friends, and a Mystery

On his first night on board Endeavour (one of a fleet of ten Galaxy Class space craft), Tirok enjoyed the strange newness of his small bedroom. He was intrigued by the warm

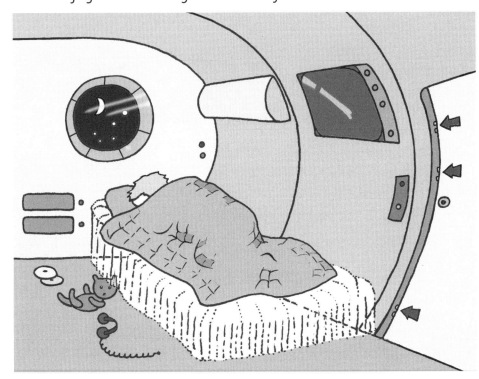

air mattress on which he could sleep, the thick, but amazingly clear porthole through which he could gaze at the myriad of small twinkling stars and of course the gleaming of the shimmering curved wall of the little room.

Tirok slept well, but woke very early, confused at first as his eyes opened on the strange surroundings. Then it hit him, he was on the

Endeavour, heading for Earth. He had left all his friends behind and thought he was in for a lonely, boring few weeks. He couldn't have been more wrong!

Over breakfast, his parents suggested he might like to explore the ship whilst they went to the shops on board to stock up on some of the things they might need during their voyage. Tirok was surprised and rather pleased that they would let him go off alone for a while on the enormous craft. He was given a plan of the ship with all the public areas marked on it. He quickly decided to start by investigating the 'Under 13's Museum of Space', as he could have fun there and learn a bit about the planets past which they would travel. After hastily finishing breakfast, Tirok washed, dressed and carefully followed the signs to his destination.

He had a brilliant morning. There were interactive displays, holographic planet scenes and, most importantly, new friends. There were other youngsters who, like him, thought the journey would be a solitary experience. Unlike on Gatteoc his companions on this voyage were, in the main, humans. On entering his first holographic planetary experience, he was so preoccupied looking at the sky effects that he bumped into Jen.

Jen was an earth girl, a few months older than Tirok and about three centimetres taller. She had a mischievous smile and a quick sense of humour.

"Look where you're going you clumsy clot!" she giggled, rubbing her arm where he collided with her, but grinning with amusement as she did so. "You'll have to get used to looking in front of you to make it back to earth without bruising all the other passengers." At this they both chuckled, and knew immediately that they were destined to be friends.

Later that morning, whilst enjoying the interactive display about the earth's solar system, they met Sote, one of the only young passengers not originating from Earth. He was about their height, and happily, though a rather unusual blobby shape, he had eyes, hearing apparatus and a mouth at what we would think of as head level. His many arms were quite short, and each of them finished in three long fingers. At the base of his body were numerous short legs, with toes spread from them rather like starfish. As the children soon discovered, these features made him very adept at ball games, and an exceedingly fast runner.

The three youngsters, after a very entertaining and informative morning, navigated their way towards the cafe for a snack. On the way there, something most unusual occurred, the significance of which was not immediately apparent. As they were walking along Floating Walkway Number 17, on Deck 42, the lights flickered. Just one person would have thought they had imagined it, but when the three of them noticed a flickering then it most definitely had happened. After the momentary lighting anomaly, the walkway seemed to wobble slightly, then all seemed well again.

"That was spooky!" exclaimed Tirok. "I wonder what caused it."

"Probably just a blip in the power," replied Sote.

That would have been the end of it but for what they noticed next.

"Look!" gasped Jen in a surprised whisper. "Where did that appear from?"

There on the left of them was another walkway, one that certainly hadn't been there a few moments ago, floating silently at right angles to their own. They checked their plan of the ship. It wasn't marked at all, and none of them recalled seeing it on their way to the museum that morning.

They all knew that the sensible thing to do would be to continue on their route to the cafe, but they were curious. Some might say too curious for their own good. What was it doing there? Why and how had it appeared? There was only one way to find out. So with the sense of safety that being in a group affords, they cautiously set off down the tunnel.

○ Name the three central characters in this chapter.

_____

○ What was the name of the space craft on which they were travelling?

_____

○ What type of space craft was it?

_____

○ Why was Tirok surprised when his parents suggested he might like to explore the ship?

_____

_____

○ What did Tirok use to find his way around the space ship?

_____

○ Where did he decide to go first?

_____

○ What did Jen call Tirok when he bumped into her?

_____

○ What was Sote very good at doing?

_____

○ What adverb, at the end of the chapter, tells the reader how the three young travellers set off down the mysterious walkway?   _____

○ Write the meaning of these words found in the text.

mischievous   _____

exceedingly   _____

recalled   _____

○ On the back of this sheet, list all the describing words you can find in the text.

○   Find a word in the text that is an anagram of **toes**. _____

○   List four words from the text that are used instead of 'said'.

   _____   _____

   _____   _____

○   Write the line, found early in the text, that reminds the reader that Tirok's journey would not be a boring one.

   _____

   _____

○   Why do you think the author refers to 'hearing apparatus', rather than using the word 'ears'?

   _____

   _____

○   Why do you think the author chooses to finish the chapter at the point he/she does?

   _____

   _____

○   Why do you think the 'address' of the floating walkway they were on, Walkway 17, Deck 42, has been given?

   _____

   _____

○   Write a definition for each of these words from the text:

   myriad _____

   _____

   anomaly _____

   _____

   adept _____

   _____

○   On the back of the sheet, or in your exercise book, write the third chapter of the story. Bear in mind all the information that you have been given so far.

This unit addresses the Literacy Strategy:
Term 2 objective   5: to understand the use of figurative language in poetry and prose; compare poetic phrasing with narrative/descriptive examples; locate use of simile.
Term 3 objective   5: to clap out and count syllables in each line of regular poetry.
Term 3 objective   6: to describe how a poet does or does not use rhyme, e.g. every alternate line, rhyming couplets, no rhyme, other patterns of rhyme.

English Autumn

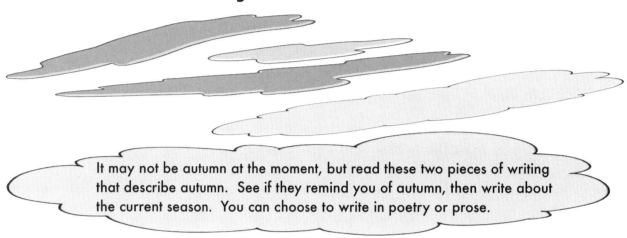

It may not be autumn at the moment, but read these two pieces of writing that describe autumn. See if they remind you of autumn, then write about the current season. You can choose to write in poetry or prose.

Clouds chase in silence,
Across the clear blue sky.
Giraffe-like shadows,
Grow longer with the day.
Overgrown flowers
Flutter and breathe their last -
Late buds will never open now,
Keeping their secrets
Like unopened presents.

Fruit-filled boughs hang low,
Waiting to be picked.
Golden sun-soaked crops
In waves stirred by the breeze.
Precious sunny days
Entice you out of doors,
Like the Pied Piper on his flute.
But chill winds will warn
That winter follows soon.

SIGNS OF AUTUMN

The sun is low in the sky and the shadows are lengthening, sure signs that Summer is turning into Autumn. The leaves are still green, but darker and dull. Their edges are turning brown.

Apples, pears and plums hang heavy as lead, making the boughs bend towards the ground. A few fallen leaves scamper across the grass like mice, stopping and starting, powered by the wind.

From inside, through my window, the sunshine looks as warm and inviting as any summer's day, but I step outside and return for a jumper for protection against the chilly breeze.

The grass is damp and the air is full of the smell of harvest. The hedgerow is laden with hops, elderberries, blackberries and autumn flowering honeysuckle. Oak, beech and chestnut are decorated with nuts, still green, waiting to ripen and turn brown.

The colours of autumn are beautiful but winter will not be far behind.

1. The poem 'English Autumn' does not rhyme but it does have a pattern. Count the syllables in each line of the poem and write it down at the end of each line to find the pattern like this:-

Number of syllables

1   1 1 1 1

Clouds chase in silence,   **5**

1 1 1 1   1   1

Across the clear blue sky.   **6**

Giraffe-like shadows,

Grow longer with the day.

Overgrown flowers

Flutter and breathe their last -

Late buds will never open now,

Keeping their secrets

Like unopened presents.

Fruit-filled boughs hang low,

Waiting to be picked.

Golden sun-soaked crops

In waves stirred by the breeze.

Precious sunny days

Entice you out of doors,

Like the Pied Piper on his flute.

But chill winds will warn

That winter follows soon.

2.   List four 'Signs of Autumn' found in the piece of prose.

1. _____

2. _____

3. _____

4. _____

SIMILES

Similes are used in writing to compare one thing with another. For example:

> The night was as black as coal.
> The wind was as cold as ice.
> The leopard ran like the wind.
> The sea sparkled like jewels.

The words 'as' or 'like' are often used.

3.   The poem says,

'Giraffe-like shadows'

meaning that the shadows are long and thin like a giraffe.

Find another simile in the poem.

_____

4.   In the 'Signs of Autumn' the author says,
'leaves scamper across the grass like mice'.
Why does she say the leaves are like mice?

_____

_____

_____

5.   Find another simile in the prose passage and write it here.

_____

6.   Invent a simile of your own.

_____

This unit addresses the Literacy Strategy:
Term 2 objective   6: to identify clues which suggest poems are older, e.g. language use, vocabulary, archaic words.
Term 2 objective   7: to identify different patterns of rhyme and verse in poetry, e.g. choruses, rhyming couplets, alternate line rhymes and to
                      read these aloud effectively.

Name   **Bits and Pieces**

On this page and the next you will find a selection of poems,
limericks and tongue-twisters.

Enjoy reading them all.

Then answer the questions.

TIME TO RISE

A birdie with a yellow bill
Hopped upon the window sill,
Cocked his shining eye and said:
"Ain't you 'shamed, you sleepy-head!"

R L Stevenson

O Hush Thee, My Babie

O Hush thee, my babie, thy sire was a knight,
Thy mother a lady, both lovely and bright;
The woods and the glens, from the towers which we see,
They all are belonging, dear babie, to thee.

O fear not the bugle, though loudly it blows,
It calls but the warders that guard thy repose;
Their bows would be bended, their blades would be red,
Ere the step of a foeman drew near to thy bed.

O hush thee, my babie, the time soon will come,
When they sleep shall be broken by trumpet and drum;
Then hush thee, my darling, take rest while you may,
For strife comes with manhood, and waking with day.

Sir Walter Scott

THE SWING

How do you like to go up in a swing,
    Up in the air so blue?
Oh, I do think it the pleasantest thing
    Ever a child can do!

Up in the air and over the wall,
    Till I can see so wide,
Rivers, and trees and cattle and all
    Over the countryside -

Till I look down on the garden green,
    Down on the roof so brown -
Up in the air I go flying again,
    Up in the air and down!

R L Stevenson

The Fire

The fire is a monster
Roaring up the chimney
The fire is a monster
Glaring at the door
The fire is a monster
With its red toes curling
The fire is a monster
Spitting at the floor

MAD HABITS

There was a young lady from Norwich
Who liked eating baked beans with porridge
Which she sucked from a fork
Whilst trying to talk
That barmy young lady from Norwich.

Peter Piper picked a peck of pickled pepper;
A peck of pickled pepper Peter Piper picked;
If Peter Piper picked a peck of pickled pepper,
Where's the peck of pickled pepper Peter Piper picked?

1.   Name the poem that uses alliteration.

        _____

2.   How can you tell that 'O Hush Thee, My Babie' was written a long time ago (about 200 years ago)?

        _____

        _____

3.   Write the modern word that means the same as each of the following.

     (babie) → _____   (repose) → _____

     (ere) → _____   (foeman) → _____

     (sire) → _____   (strife) → _____

4.   What type of building (in 'O Hush Thee, My Babie') was the baby in?

        _____

5.   Which poem uses <u>metaphor</u>?

        _____

6.   Count the number of syllables in each line of the poem 'The Fire'?

     line 1 ☐   **line 2** ☐   **line 3** ☐   **line 4** ☐

     line 5 ☐   **line 6** ☐   **line 7** ☐   **line 8** ☐

7.   Which lines provide the rhyme in the poem, and what are the words?

        _____

8.   Which two poems are written in rhyming couplets?

        _____

9.   Which poem uses an alternate line rhyming pattern?

        _____

10.   Use the structure (e.g. the rhyming pattern and rhythm) of one of the poems, as a starting point to write a poem of your own.

11. Look at the poem 'Time to Rise'.
Who wrote the poem? _____

12. Name another poem written by him. _____

13. Put a ring around the correct description
of the rhyming pattern in 'Time to Rise'.

alternate line rhymes

non rhyming

rhyming couplets

14. Now ring the correct description of the
rhyming pattern in 'The Swing'.

alternate line rhymes

non rhyming

rhyming couplets

15. One of the poems was written by Sir Walter Scott. He lived from
1771 until 1832.
Which of the poems did he write?

_____

16. What type of poem is 'Mad Habits'? (Ring the correct answer.)

nursery rhyme   **ode**   **song**   **limerick**

17. Which of the poems is also a tongue-twister?

_____

18. In the limerick, what word is used to rhyme with Norwich?

_____

19. On the back:
Either, look in poetry books for more limericks
and choose your favourite to write out and illustrate;

Or, write a limerick of your own, beginning -

There was an old man in New York,
Who taught his pet parrot to talk,

Now you finish it!

This unit addresses the Literacy Strategy:
Term 2 objective   6: to identify clues which suggest poems are older, e.g. language use, vocabulary, archaic words.
Term 2 objective   7: to identify different patterns of rhyme and verse in poetry, e.g. choruses, rhyming couplets, alternate line rhymes and to read aloud effectively.
Term 3 objective   6: to describe how a poet does or does not use rhyme, e.g. every alternate line, rhyming couplets, no rhyme, other patterns of rhyme.

Edward Lear (1812-1888)

How Pleasant to Know Mr.Lear!

"How pleasant to know Mr.Lear!"
      Who has written such volumes of stuff!
Some think him ill-tempered and queer,
      But a few think him pleasant enough.

His mind is concrete and fastidious,
      His nose is remarkably big;
His visage is more or less hideous,
      His beard it resembles a wig.

He has ears, and two eyes, and ten fingers,
      Leastways if you reckon two thumbs;
Long ago he was one of the singers,
      But now he is one of the dumbs.

He sits in a beautiful parlour,
      With hundreds of books on the wall;
He drinks a great deal of Marsala,
      But never gets tipsy at all.

He has many friends, lay men and clerical,
      Old Foss is the name of his cat;
His body is perfectly spherical,
      He weareth a runcible hat.

When he walks in waterproof white,
      The children run after him so!
Calling out, "He's gone out in his night-
      Gown, that crazy old Englishman, oh!"

He weeps by the side of the ocean,
      He weeps on the top of the hill;
He purchases pancakes and lotion,
      And chocolate shrimps from the mill.

He reads, but he cannot speak, Spanish,
      He cannot abide ginger beer:
Ere the days of his pilgrimage vanish,
      How pleasant to know Mr. Lear!

The Owl and the Pussy-Cat

The Owl and the Pussy-Cat went to sea
In a beautiful pea-green boat:
They took some honey, and plenty of money
Wrapped up in a five-pound note.
The Owl looked up to the stars above,
And sang to a small guitar,
"O lovely Pussy, O Pussy, my love,
What a beautiful Pussy you are,
You are,
You are!
What a beautiful Pussy you are!"

Pussy said to the Owl, "You elegant fowl,
How charmingly sweet you sing!
Oh! let us be married; too long we have tarried:
But what shall we do for a ring?"
They sailed away, for a year and a day,
To the land where the bong-tree grows;
And there in a wood a Piggy-wig stood,
With a ring at the end of his nose,
His nose,
His nose,
With a ring at the end of his nose.

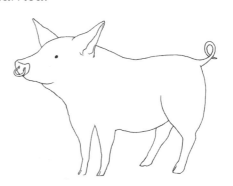

"Dear Pig, are you willing to sell for one shilling
Your ring?" Said the Piggy, "I will."
So they took it away, and were married next day
By the Turkey who lives on the hill.
They dined on mince and slices of quince,
Which they ate with a runcible spoon;
And hand in hand on the edge of the sand
They danced by the light of the moon,
The moon,
The moon,
They danced by the light of the moon.

Read the poem called 'How Pleasant to Know Mr. Lear!', an amusing poem which Edward Lear has written about himself.

1. Write down the meaning of the following words in the poem.

    fastidious : _____

    _____

    visage : _____

    _____

    parlour : _____

    _____

    ere : _____

    _____

2. Pick out three words which show us that the poem is old.

    _____   _____   _____

3. In verse 6:   *When he walks in waterproof white,*
    The children run after him so!
    Calling out, "He's gone out in his night-
    Gown, that crazy old Englishman, oh!"

    Why did the poet split up the word night-gown on to separate lines?

    _____

    _____

    _____

4. What is the pattern of rhyme in the poem 'How Pleasant to know Mr Lear'?

    ☐ **rhyming couplet**   ☐ **1st and last line of each verse**

    ☐ **alternate line rhymes**

5. Write a short poem in the style of Edward Lear called
    'How Pleasant to Know ....' and then your own name.
    Use the back of this sheet.

Read the poem by Edward Lear called 'The Owl and the Pussy-Cat'.

1.   What did the Owl and the Pussy-Cat take with them in their boat?

_____

_____

2.   Where did they get their wedding ring from?

_____

_____

3.   What did the Owl and the Pussy-Cat eat after the wedding?

_____

_____

4.   This poem has a more complicated rhyming pattern than 'How Pleasant to Know Mr. Lear'. Pick out the words in the Owl and the Pussy-Cat that Edward Lear has chosen to rhyme with the words in boxes on the left.

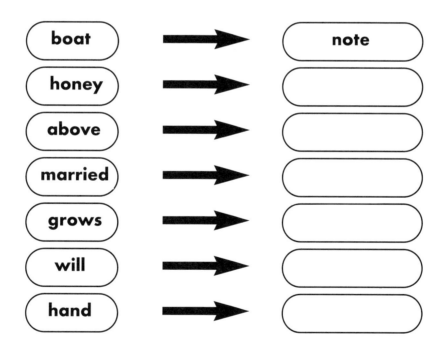

boat   →   note
honey   →
above   →
married →
grows   →
will   →
hand   →

5.   Find 2 words in the poem that you would be unlikely to find in a modern poem.

_____   _____

6.   Practise reciting the poem, making use of the rhyming words and the repeated phrases at the end of each verse, to add expression to your recital.

This unit addresses the Literacy Strategy:
Term 2 objective 15: appraise a non-fiction book for its contents and usefulness by scanning, e.g. headings, contents list.
Term 2 objective 17: to scan texts in print or on screen to locate key words or phrases, useful headings and key sentences and to use these as a tool for summarising text.
Term 2 objective 18: to mark extracts by annotating and by selecting key headings, word or sentences, or alternatively, noting these.

Harry Houdini
The Man who Defied Death

Who was Harry Houdini?

Harry Houdini was a world famous magician. He could escape from handcuffs, locked boxes and ropes tied about him, in such a short space of time that his audience were left both astonished and amazed. Houdini was born in 1874 in Budapest in Hungary, but moved to the United States when he was four years old.

His real name was Ehrich Weiss, but he used the name, Harry Houdini, when he became an escapologist and a magician in 1891. He claimed that all his tricks were easily explained, and often told people how many of them were done. He was extremely fit and strong, and could untie knots through a thick bag that he had been tied inside. He could also use his teeth to untie knots, and his feet were nearly as useful as his hands in helping him to escape.

Harry had spent a long time as he grew up, learning how to undo any lock with out a key, (this is called picking a lock). This meant that he could escape from any handcuffs or locked chains, very easily. He even asked his audience to bring along their own locks for him to use in his show, just to prove that he wasn't using trick locks.

Escapes from Water

One of Houdini's favourite tricks, was to get into a large iron can (like an old fashioned milk churn) which was just about big enough for him to crouch down inside. The can could be seen by the audience, and they watched as Houdini was handcuffed. Next, the can was filled with water and a lid fastened on the top with several locks. A curtain was pulled in front of the can and music played. After three and a half minutes, Houdini came from behind the curtain, in his bathing costume, dripping with water. The people in the audience were staggered. A similar trick to this was one where he had his feet locked into a wooden block and was lowered head first into a tank full of water. Even to this day, not many people know how he escaped from this trick.

Another time, Houdini was tied and locked into a packing case, that had heavy weights inside it. The case was then wrapped with steel tape, and dropped into the harbour near New York city. The watching crowd were amazed to see him reappear on the surface of the water in less than one minute.

Leaping from Bridges

In 1906, Harry hit on the idea of drawing attention to his show by jumping off bridges, into a river below. Sometimes he was weighed down with an iron ball, but he was always handcuffed or tied with chains. Houdini could escape so quickly, that he was often free from his handcuffs before he touched the water. A huge crowd would always gather to see his amazing performances. His wife, Bess, who he had married at the age of twenty, would often be there to see her husband defy death.

Films

In 1921, he set up his own film company, to make films that had exciting escapes as a part of the story. Houdini himself did all the escapes and tricks, but found that he did not enjoy the rest of the acting. His company did well at first, but it was a failure in the end and lost him a lot of money.

Death

All his life, Houdini had faced danger, but in the end, he did not die directly from one of his tricks. He had always said that he could be punched in the stomach without feeling any pain. He did this by preparing his stomach muscles, and holding them tight in a special way. Houdini needed time to prepare his body in this way, but one day a student punched him, very hard, before he had time to do this. Houdini did not think that he had been badly hurt, but he collapsed two days later and died on October 31st 1926.

Here is the contents page of the book that the information about Harry Houdini came from. It is a book all about different kinds of famous people.

CONTENTS

1. Scan quickly through the text about Harry Houdini, and then write a few
    sentences saying what you think it is about.

    _____

    _____

    _____

    _____

    _____

2. Read through the text, and underline any words or phrases, that tell us something
    about Harry Houdini's life, that are not to do with his tricks.

3. Now complete this timeline to show some major dates in his life.

    BORN   **MOVED TO USA**   **MARRIED**

    Date [_____]   [_____]   [_____]

    STARTED JUMPING   SET UP FILM
    OFF BRIDGES   COMPANY   **DIED**

    Date [_____]   [_____]   [_____]

4. Under which sub-heading in the text would you look to find the information
    about Houdini's trick with the water-filled iron can?

    _____

5. Under each of the five sub-headings, copy the words, phrases or sentences that
    you think are most important in that section.

    Who was Harry Houdini? _____

    _____

    _____

    Escapes from Water _____

    _____

    _____

    Leaping from Bridges _____

    _____

    _____

© Andrew Brodie Publications ✓ www.acblack.com

Films _____

_____

_____

Death _____

_____

_____

6.   Now write a short paragraph about the life of Harry Houdini.

_____

_____

_____

_____

_____

_____

_____

_____

_____

7.   Look at the contents page. On which pages
      might you find information about Harry Houdini? _____

8.   What would you expect to find on page 35?

_____

9.   Name two people that you would expect to read about on these pages.

Page 36 _____   _____

Page 14 _____   _____

Page 22 _____   _____

10.   On the back of this sheet put the contents list into alphabetical order.

This unit addresses the Literacy Strategy:
Term 1 objective 19: to understand and use the terms fact and opinion, and to begin to distinguish the two in reading and other media.
Term 2 objective 20: to identify the key features of explanatory texts.

YEAR	UNIT	Sheet
4	18	A

Name

A Brief Guide to the Solar System

The **solar system** is the name given to the **Sun** and the objects that orbit it. There are many objects that travel around, or orbit, the sun, but the main ones are the nine planets that we know of. One of these is, of course, our **Earth**. The other eight are **Mercury**, **Venus**, **Mars**, **Jupiter**, **Saturn**, **Uranus**, **Neptune**, and **Pluto**. Scientists believe that only our Earth is capable of sustaining life.

The Sun

The Sun is a massive ball of burning gases. Its warmth and light sustain life on Earth. The Sun is many times bigger that our Earth - if you imagine Earth to be a golf ball the Sun would be the size of a football. It is about ninety-three million miles away from us. In reality the Sun is a star much like the countless other stars you see when you look into the night sky.

The Hot Planets

In our solar system the closest planet to the Sun is Mercury. The planet Mercury is smaller than Earth and far too hot to sustain life as we know it. As a year is the time it takes for a planet to orbit the Sun, Mercury, being close to the Sun, has a year of just eighty-eight days.

The next closest planet to the Sun is Venus and is quite easy to see in the sky, even without a telescope. Venus is the bright planet that sometimes is visible at dusk and sometimes at dawn. For this reason it is sometimes referred to as the evening star or sometimes as the morning star. Venus is also an extremely hot planet, unsuitable for any form of known life to survive. Venus has a two hundred and twenty-five day year as this is the length of time it takes to orbit the Sun.

The next planet we would meet if we were journeying away from the Sun would be our own planet, Earth. As you no doubt know it has an orbit that takes three hundred and sixty-five and a quarter days. You also know that the distance from the Sun, and hence the conditions on Earth, make it suitable to sustain life. If that was not the case you would not be reading this text - indeed this text would not exist!

Travelling further from the Earth you next encounter Mars, also known as the red planet. Looking at Mars it is obvious why it is known as the red planet. In fact it was named after the Roman god of war because of its blood-like colour. For many years people believed that there could be life on Mars, though more recently scientists (aided by space probes) have found no real evidence to support this.

The Cold Planets

As one travels a lot further away from the Sun, the planets become much colder. The next planet we meet on our journey is Jupiter, the largest of the planets in our solar system, with a diameter of over one hundred and forty-two thousand kilometres, or to look at it another way, a diameter more than ten times that of our Earth. The planet Jupiter looks bright yellow, and has not one moon (as our Earth does) but sixteen.

Next we come to Saturn, famed for its rings. These rings that encircle the planet are actually formed from tiny pieces of dust and ice. Saturn has even more moons than Jupiter, as it has twenty in total.

Uranus is yet further from the Sun and is another very large planet with fifteen moons. Uranus is surrounded by very dark rings.

Similar in size to Uranus is the next planet Neptune. Being so very far from the Sun its orbit takes a very long time; approximately one hundred and sixty five of our Earth years.

The final planet that we know orbits our Sun is the planet Pluto. It is much smaller than the other four cold planets; in fact it is even smaller than the moon that orbits our Earth.

Perhaps there are more planets in our solar system, (remember that to be part of our solar system a planet must orbit our Sun) but if so they are so distant that our scientists have not yet found them.

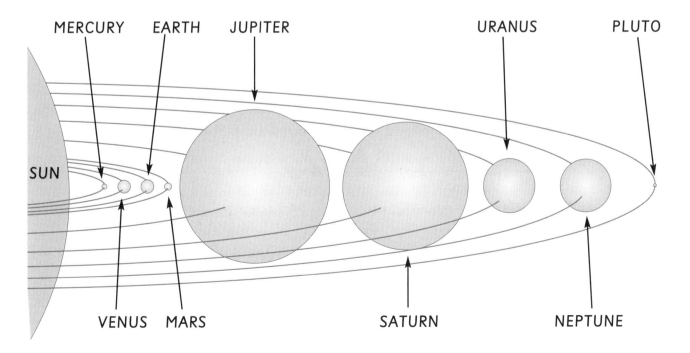

The picture is not to scale, but gives some indication of comparative sizes.

Name _____   The Solar System

✳ Circle the words that best describe how this text is written:

past tense   **present tense**   **future tense**

✳ Circle the word that best describes the text:

poetry   **fiction**   **opinion**   **fact**

✳ How many planets are in our solar system? _____

✳ Name the planet closest to the Sun.   _____

✳ Which planet is sometimes known as the morning
star, and sometimes as the evening star?   _____

✳ Which planet is further from the Sun than Venus,
but closer to the Sun than Mars?   _____

✳ Which planet is known as the red planet?   _____

✳ Name the largest planet in the solar system.   _____

✳ Name the five planets that are known as the cold planets due to their great
distance from the Sun.

_____   _____   _____

_____   _____

✳ How long does it take the planet Neptune to orbit the Sun?

_____

✳ Write the names of the planets in the order of their distances from the Sun.

1. _____   2. _____   3. _____

4. _____   5. _____   6. _____

7. _____   8. _____   9. _____

✳ Name two features of the text that help the reader to understand that this is an information text.

_____

_____

✳ Explain how the writer has decided to divide the information into paragraphs.

_____

_____

_____

✳ Why are the names of the planets in bold type in the first paragraph?

_____

_____

_____

✳ Do you think the diagram of the solar system helps the reader to understand the text? Give reasons for your answer.

_____

_____

_____

✳ Explain what the term 'year' means.

_____

_____

_____

✳ Explain the meaning of the word 'orbit'.

_____

_____

_____

✳ In the text, how did the author decide in what order to write about the planets?

_____

_____

✳ Use information books to find out more, then write about one of the planets in our solar system.

This unit addresses the Literacy Strategy:
Term 3 objective   1: to identify social, moral or cultural issues in stories, e.g. the dilemmas faced by characters or the moral of the story, and to discuss how the characters deal with them; to locate evidence in text.
Term 3 objective   8: to write critically about an issue or dilemma raised in a story, explaining the problem, alternative courses of action and evaluating the writer's solution.

Sam's Diary

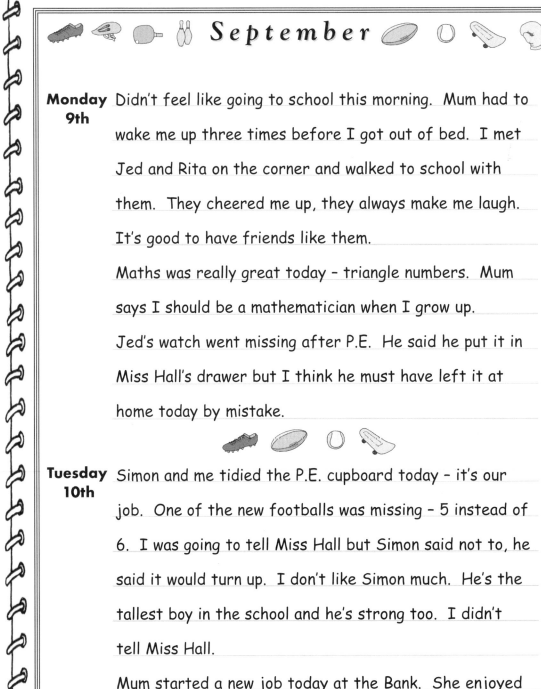

September

Monday 9th Didn't feel like going to school this morning. Mum had to wake me up three times before I got out of bed. I met Jed and Rita on the corner and walked to school with them. They cheered me up, they always make me laugh. It's good to have friends like them.

Maths was really great today – triangle numbers. Mum says I should be a mathematician when I grow up.

Jed's watch went missing after P.E. He said he put it in Miss Hall's drawer but I think he must have left it at home today by mistake.

Tuesday 10th Simon and me tidied the P.E. cupboard today – it's our job. One of the new footballs was missing – 5 instead of 6. I was going to tell Miss Hall but Simon said not to, he said it would turn up. I don't like Simon much. He's the tallest boy in the school and he's strong too. I didn't tell Miss Hall.

Mum started a new job today at the Bank. She enjoyed it so she cooked Spaghetti Bolognaise for tea to celebrate, my favourite!

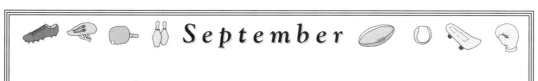

S e p t e m b e r

Wednesday 11th   This week is not going well. I went back into the classroom at lunchtime to get my inhaler. Simon was in there by Miss Hall's desk. I think he shut the desk drawer when he saw me through the door. He had a pen in his hand. He said he was just going to put it away. When he opened his drawer to put it in I saw, or thought I saw, what looked like the strap of Jed's watch.

Thursday 12th   After register this morning Miss Hall asked Simon and I if we noticed how many footballs there were when we tidied the P.E. cupboard on Tuesday.

Simon said we didn't count them. I stayed behind at break so that I was the only one left in the class with Miss Hall. I told her that there were only 5 footballs on Tuesday and she seemed a bit cross and asked why I hadn't told her that when she asked.

Then, when I walked home with Rita, we passed Simon's house and he was kicking a football up against a wall.

Read the extract from Sam's Diary.

1. Do we know if Sam is a boy or a girl?

   ☐ **Sam is a boy**

   ☐ **Sam is a girl**

   ☐ **We don't know if Sam is a boy or a girl.**

2. Who did Sam walk to school with on Monday?

   _____

3. What does Sam think about Rita and Jed as friends?

   _____

   _____

   _____

4. How do you think Sam feels about Simon? How do you know?

   _____

   _____

   _____

5. What does Sam think may have happened to Jed's watch, the pen and the football?

   _____

   _____

   _____

6. Read the extract for Wednesday again. What would you have done on Wednesday if you had found Simon in the classroom?

   _____

   _____

   _____

7. If you were Sam's friend what would you advise Sam to do now?

   _____

   _____

   _____

8. Write Sam's entry into his diary for Friday. What do you think could happen? How could Sam sort out his concerns?
   NOTE - You may like to discuss questions 7 and 8 with a partner first.

September

Friday 13th

9. If you had a diary, what would you write for today?

This unit addresses the Literacy Strategy:
Term 1 objective   1: to investigate how settings and characters are built up from small details, and how the reader responds to them.
Term 3 objective   1: to identify social, moral or cultural issues in stories, e.g. the dilemmas faced by characters or the moral of the story, and to discuss how the characters deal with them; to locate evidence in text.

YEAR	UNIT	Sheet
4	**20**	**A**

Name   Grandad

Grandad

My Grandad is great. He lives round the corner from me in the house my Mum used to live in when she was a girl. It's old-fashioned compared to my house but I love it. It never changes.

I go to Grandad's every day, after school, until Mum and Dad get home from work. He's always pleased to see me and has the kettle on ready to make a cup of tea, which we have with a chocolate biscuit.

He lets me make pizzas or cakes in his kitchen and doesn't mind if I make a mess. I love doing art so he keeps thick, white paper, paints and every size of brush, and will lay out newspaper on the dining table for me to paint on. He thinks my pictures are as good as Picasso's and puts them on the kitchen wall. He says he'll never need to decorate the kitchen, he just keeps putting up my pictures.

When I go to see Grandad in the holidays he takes me out in his Morris Minor. He's had it since 1963 but it's his pride and joy. It's shiny, pale blue with blue

leather seats. I have to sit on a cushion because it has a dip in it where Grandma used to sit.

Sometimes we go fishing; Grandad and me will sit by the river all day; eating sandwiches, drinking lemonade and then go home with nothing. We always put back everything we catch. Grandad says we can always tell Mum and Dad about 'the one that got away'! He puts his hands out in front of him, half a metre apart, to show how big the imaginary fish is. I smile.

Mum says Grandad misses Grandma. She says he gets lonely and sad, but he never shows me.

He talks about her a lot and sometimes talks to her picture hanging on the wall as if she was still alive. He says, 'Now Mary, how do I cook these beans?' or 'I've put the duster round for you, Mary.'

I miss Grandma too but Grandad says we'll never forget her.

1. Why does the child in the story think his Grandad is great?

_____

_____

_____

2. Why does the child go to his Grandad's every day after school?

_____

_____

_____

3. What does the child do at Grandad's?

_____

_____

_____

4. What does Grandad think of his Grandchild's paintings?

_____

_____

_____

5. Why does the child have to sit on a cushion in the Morris Minor car?

_____

_____

_____

6. Why does Grandad get sad and lonely sometimes?

_____

_____

_____

7. Why do you think Grandad often talks about Grandma or talks to her picture?

_____

_____

_____

8. Why do you think Grandad is always pleased to see his Grandchild?

_____

_____

_____

Name

Grandad

Write about somebody special in your family. Where do they live? How often do you see them? What do they look like?

_____

_____

_____

_____

_____

_____

_____

_____

_____

_____

_____

_____

_____

_____

_____

_____

_____

_____

_____

_____

_____

_____

_____

_____

_____

_____

Name

The Ordeal of Robin Hood

from 'Please Mrs Butler' by Allan Ahlberg

(1) There is a new boy in our class;
He came the other day.
He hadn't any friends, of course,
So we let him be in our play.

That was the first mistake we made.

(2) The play was called 'Bold Robin Hood';
We'd practised it all week.
The new boy missed rehearsals
So he had no lines to speak.

He thought of a few, though, as you will see.

(3) Besides, this boy was foreign,
His English wasn't good.
He said his name was Janek;
He'd not heard of Robin Hood.

Robin Hood didn't get to Poland, Miss Hodge said.

(4) Well, first we pushed the desks back
To make a bigger space.
Then we hung this curtain up
For the outlaws' hiding place.

Miss Hodge just let us get on with it.

(5) Kevin Jukes was Robin Hood,
Roy was Little John,
I was the Sheriff of Nottingham -
I had this red cloak on.

The new boy was one of my guards, supposedly.

(6) The swords we had were rulers;
The cupboard, Robin's den;
And most of us had moustaches
Drawn with black felt pen.

Roy's was navy blue, but you could hardly tell.

7. The rest of the class sat round to watch,
Miss Hodge was watching too.
Then Keith announced the title
And who was playing who.

Keith was also Friar Tuck with a cushion up his coat.

8. At first it all went pretty well,
Mistakes we made were slight;
The trouble only started
When we got to the first fight.

There should have been three fights altogether; should have been.

9. What we'd practised was an ambush
To rescue Friar Tuck,
With me and my guards just riding by
Until the outlaws struck.

No horses, of course, just 'clip-clop' noises.

10. So there was I, my cloak tossed back,
Duelling with Robin Hood;
While Janek - I didn't know it then -
Was guarding me more than he should.

Perhaps there's nothing in the Polish language for 'Aaargh!'

11. Guards, you see, are meant to fight
For a little while, then lose.
Get captured, killed or wounded,
Whatever way they choose.

Usually our plays had guns in them, only this time Miss Hodge said she was sick of guns.

12. But Janek wasn't having that,
He wouldn't even defend;
And the way he was generally carrying on,
The play would never end.

That was the second mistake we made: it ended all right.

13. And still the worst was yet to come
In Robin Hood's ordeal:
Not only wouldn't Janek die,
He was sword-fighting for real!

The Merrie Men were looking less merry by the minute.

(14.) Will Scarlett's hand was stinging
From the blows that Janek smote,
And Friar Tuck was thankful
For that cushion up his coat.

Alan-a-Dale and Little John were already behind the curtain.

(15.) We did our best to stop him;
Tried 'whispering' in his ear;
But he was shouting foreign words,
We couldn't make him hear.

I could see then how Poland knocked us out of the World Cup.

(16.) The play was going haywire now,
The audience could tell.
When some of the guards tried changing sides,
Janek polished them off as well.

'Pole-ished' - get it? Keith thought of that on the way home.

(17.) Then, having done for the outlaws,
He shoved me out of the way
And had a go at Robin Hood.
That wasn't part of the play!

In my opinion, Miss Hodge should have stopped it then.

(18.) Now Kevin had this plastic sword
(The play was his idea)
And being who he was, of course,
Was supposed to show no fear.

I was showing fear, and Janek was on my side.

(19.) But once the sword was broke in half,
And minus his Merrie Men,
Robin Hood dropped the other half
And surrendered there and then.

Then Miss Hodge stopped it, which I thought was a bit late.

(20) Anyway, that was the end of that.
The audience gave us a clap.
Me and Roy took the curtain down
And joined the rush for the tap.

It's thirsty work, acting; and we had our moustaches to wash off.

'The Ordeal of Robin Hood' reproduced from 'Please Mrs Butler' by Allan Ahlberg (Kestrel 1983). © Allan Ahlberg, 1983. Reproduced by kind permission of Penguin Books Ltd.

'The Ordeal of Robin Hood' reproduced from 'Please Mrs Butler' by Allan Ahlberg (Kestrel 1983). © Allan Ahlberg, 1983. Reproduced by kind permission of Penguin Books Ltd.

21. Roy also fetched the first-aid box,
Put a plaster on his shin,
And offered to settle Kevin's nerves
With a junior aspirin.

Kevin was worried what his Mum was going to say about the sword.

22. Janek, meanwhile, was prowling round
With *his* sword still in his hand;
Suspecting another ambush, perhaps,
From another outlaw band.

Miss Hodge said he reminded her of Errol Flynn, whoever he was.

23. Keith said, let's wait for the Christmas play
And have Janek in again.
He'd make mincemeat of the shepherds,
And slaughter the Three Wise Men.

He'd be worse than Herod, Keith said.

24. But I'm about fed up with plays;
Football's a better bet.
Now we've got this match against Class 4
And we've never beaten them yet.

You can probably guess what was in my mind; Roy could.

25. So tomorrow Janek brings his kit
(The kick-off's half-past three);
And we'll play him in the forward line:
He's a striker …obviously.

Name _____

The Ordeal of Robin Hood

This section refers to the poem called 'The Ordeal of Robin Hood' by A. Ahlberg.

»→ What was the name of the new boy in the class? _____

»→ What country was the new boy from? _____

»→ What was the name of the teacher? _____

»→ What did the children in the play use for swords? _____

»→ Why was Friar Tuck thankful he had a cushion up his coat? (verse 14)

_____

»→ What part did the narrator have in the play?

_____

»→ The line between each verse is written in italic writing. It does not rhyme and is an amusing comment. Who do you think is making these remarks?

☐ **The teacher**

☐ **The boy playing the Sheriff of Nottingham**

☐ **The boy playing Robin Hood**

☐ **Keith**

»→ Choose one verse that you find amusing.
a) Copy it out.

_____
_____
_____
_____

b) Say why you find it funny.

_____
_____
_____

Name

The Ordeal of Robin Hood

≫→ How did Janek spoil the play? Do you think that he meant to?

_____

_____

_____

_____

≫→ The poem 'The Ordeal of Robin Hood' tells an amusing story about some children doing a play. Why do you think Allan Ahlberg chose to write this as a poem? Was it a good choice?

_____

_____

_____

_____

≫→ Find the meaning of the following words in the poem.

surrendered: _____

_____

outlaw: _____

_____

slaughtered: _____

_____

going haywire: _____

_____

defend: _____

_____

≫→ Reciting the poem.
Work in a group of 3 or 4 children. Take it in turns to read a verse. One person can read the lines in italics. Practise your verses so that you put expression in your voice.

This unit addresses the Literacy Strategy:
Term 3 objective 19: to evaluate advertisements for their impact, appeal and honesty, focusing in particular on how information about the product is presented: exaggerated claims, tactics for grabbing attention, linguistic devices, e.g. puns, jingles, alliteration, invented words.

Look at the following advertisements.

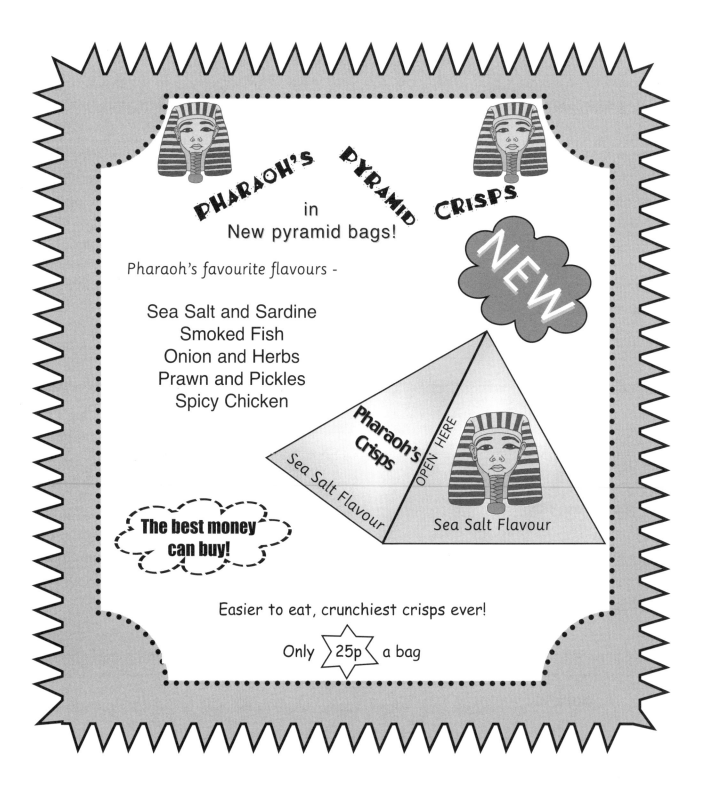

juicy apples

kiwis full of vitamin C

gorgeous grapes

FAST FOOD

Do you like fast food that gives variety from all over the globe, is nutritious, easy to eat and cheap?

Where? That's easy.

Visit your local greengrocers or the fruit and veg. section at your local supermarket. You won't do better.

crunchy celery

carrots - cheap and nutritious

 nectarines and peaches

bananas - instant energy food

Fruit and Vegetable Marketing Board

BLEE'S NEW
SUGAR FREE CHOCOLATE BAR

you'll love:

It's sugar free,
It's heavenly
Its made by Blee's
It's chocolate!

BLEE'S
CHOCOLATE
SUGAR FREE

you won't believe it can taste so delicious!

Dentists agree you are 40% less likely to need fillings if you eat BLEE'S instead of normal chocolate.

TRY IT NOW!

1. Look at the advertisement for Pharaoh's Crisps.
    Give two examples of **alliteration**, where two or more words begin with the same letter.

    1. _____

    2. _____

2. The advertisement claims that Pharaoh's Crisps are 'The best money can buy'. Write down two more claims the advert makes.

    1. _____

    2. _____

3. Now study the advertisement for 'Fast Food'. What words grab your attention when you first see the advertisement?

    ┌───┐
    │   │
    └───┘

4. Who do you think the advertisement for Fast Food is aimed at?

    _____

    _____

5. How could you improve the advertisement? Think about the text and the illustrations.

    _____

    _____

    _____

    _____

    _____

6. The advertisement for Blee's Chocolate claims that you will need less fillings at the dentist if you eat Blee's Chocolate. Do you think this is a true or false claim? Give a reason for your answer.

    _____

    _____

    _____

    _____

7.   What other information could be included in the advertisement for Blee's Chocolate?

_____

_____

_____

_____

8.   In the space below design your own advertisement for a food suitable for a packed lunch. Consider the following key points:

✳ who is the advert aimed at?
✳ use a variety of text styles and sizes
✳ use colourful illustrations to attract attention
✳ use alliteration or rhymes

This unit addresses the Literacy Strategy:
Term 3 objective 19: to evaluate advertisements for their impact, appeal and honesty, focusing in particular on how information about the product is presented: exaggerated claims, tactics for grabbing attention, linguistic devices, e.g. puns, jingles, alliteration, invented words.

YEAR 4 | **UNIT** 23 | **Sheet** A   Name   Advertising

On these pages you will see a selection of lines from advertisements.

These are often called advertising slogans.

1. Magic Muscle provides purifying power.

2. Zims will set your taste buds tingling.

3. Whizz gives you the glittering gleam of a glistening white smile.

4. Tasty goodness, bite after bite.

5. For happy pets with tails that wag,
    Feed every day with new tinned TAG.

6. Total Active Goodness is always the way,
    When your best friend eats TAG every single day.

7. Look handsome and debonair,
    Wearing _ _ _ _ in your hair.

8. Look like a demented hedgehog.
    Put _ _ _ _ in your hair each day.

9. Tebs terrific tinglers, full of fruity fizz.

10. Sally sells STICKY sweets at the local store.
    Susan sucks seven sorts and still wants more.

11.   Cleans to a super shine, every time.

12.   Serious sportsmen wear Snappies on their feet.

13.   Nibble Nettoes every morning.

14.   Lots of fruity flavours, fun for you to eat.

15.   City slickers wear Snappies for style.

16.   Magic Muscle keeps things bright.

17.   Nettoes and milk for a healthy start to your day.

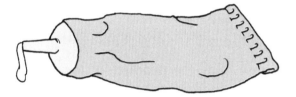

18.   'Sett' sticks to anything.

19.   TAG to make your coat shine and to help you bounce with vitality.

20.   Snappies shoes for comfort in the sun.

21.   Mmmm Zims - a taste bud sensation.

22.   Dashing dancers wear Snappies.

1. Write the slogan which is based on a well known tongue-twister.

   _____

2. Why is the word STICKY written in block capitals in slogan 10?

   _____

   _____

3. Why do you think the sweets are shaped as they are?

   _____

   _____

4. Name seven flavours you think they might be.

   _____

   _____

5. Look at slogans 7 and 8. They are both for the same product. Which do you think would be the more successful slogan? Give reasons for your answer.

   _____

   _____

   _____

6. Do you think the product in slogans 7 and 8 is aimed at males or females? Give reasons for your answer.

   _____

   _____

   _____

7. Write the slogan for the product most likely to be a toothpaste.

   _____

8. Write the numbers of all the slogans that could be advertising household cleaning products.

   _____

9. Why do the petfood makers use the phrase 'Total Active Goodness' in one of their slogans?

   _____

   _____

   _____

10. Invent names for the four types of 'Snappies' that have slogans.

11. Complete the following slogans:

   - **Magic Muscle provides** _____

   - **Magic Muscle** _____

12. What do you think 'Magic Muscle' might be?

   _____

   _____

13. Look at the slogans numbered 7 and 8. They are both for the same product. Invent a good name for the product.

   _____

14. Look at slogan number 17. What sort of product is it advertising?

   _____

   _____

15. What would you do with Zims? (numbers 2 and 21) _____

   _____

16. Write the numbers of the slogans that are advertising footwear.

   _____

17. Write the slogan that might belong to a tube of glue.

   _____

18. What is the name of the pet food advertised?

   _____

19. What sort of pet do you think it is for? Give reasons for your answer.

   _____

   _____

   _____

20. Design an advertising poster for 'Tebs Terrific Tinglers'.
    Use slogan number 9 in your advert.

LOAD OF RUBBISH

Many people believe that our rubbish is slowly killing our planet. Each human being makes their own weight in rubbish every month! Most of this is dumped and buried underground. The Earth itself can recycle, and return some waste products back into soil again. These materials are called organic materials, and all started life as either plants or animals. People can help to recycle organic material by putting vegetable and garden waste on to compost heaps, where it can rot down (decay), and make new soil. Organic waste can also be put into worm bins, where the worms turn it into new soil. Some farmers use the waste produced by animals to put onto the land, to help plants to grow well. The problem is that many materials that we use, such as plastics, are not organic and will never decay in the ground. The more things we make and use, the more we have to get rid of.

What do we do with our waste that doesn't decay?

Most of our rubbish goes into large holes in the ground, called landfill sites. The rubbish is first squashed so that it takes up less space. A layer of earth is spread over it to try and stop rats and other animals from feeding on it, and spreading germs. One of the problems with landfill sites is that they can produce a dangerous gas called methane. Another problem is that some rubbish, such as old batteries, can leak out poisonous waste. Incinerators are also used to dispose of our rubbish. These are giant machines that burn the waste, but they are expensive to run, and can produce harmful gases that go into the air. Some very poisonous waste is sealed into containers, and buried under the ground because we do not know what else to do with it. Dirty water from our houses, shops, factories and streets is cleaned at a special place called a sewage works. Here all the harmful things are taken out of the water so that it is clean again. Scrap metal from factories and cars can be recycled and special scrap metal dealers collect the metal, crush it, and then sell it to be used again.

Name _____ **Load of Rubbish**

What can you do to make less waste?

Reduce

The best way to reduce the amount of waste in the world is by using less materials. There are many ways that this can be done; here are a few ideas that we can all try. Reducing the amount of packaging used on items is just one way. Instead of buying small packets of crisps in individual bags, buy a big bag, and put them in a reusable air-tight container. Choose to buy the things that do not have too many wrappers, instead of the brands with lots of wrapping. At some shops, you can take in your used plastic or glass containers to be refilled. Only buy or take as much as you need, and that way less will be thrown out as waste. Save energy by switching off lights, and turning the heating down, and wearing warmer clothes. Many things can be mended instead of just throwing them away.

Reuse

The next best thing to reducing the amount of waste you make, is to reuse things as much as possible. Take your clothes you don't need to a charity shop to be reused, and you may be lucky and find something you want to buy there yourself. Look at your waste and see how else you can use it. Many containers can be reused for paint pots, or flower pots or other useful items. Don't waste paper, use both sides of the sheet whenever you can. Whenever possible, use recycled paper to save more trees being chopped down. You might enjoy making your own recycled paper. Envelopes can also be reused, if you open them carefully, and then use a sticky label to use them again.

Recycle

If we can't reduce or reuse our waste, then we can try to recycle it. This means using the material that something is made of to make something new. By taking glass, paper, aluminium cans and some plastic to a recycling centre, or sorting it for collection from our homes, we can ensure that it is made into new bottles, paper and cans. Although energy is used to recycle these things, less new material is used. Try to choose items that are easier to recycle such as glass bottles instead of plastic ones. In many poorer countries of the world, children make their own toys entirely out of things that are

being thrown away. They make some very clever cars and lorries out of bits of metal and old tin cans. In some countries, people do not have money to always buy new things, so they are very good at reusing materials for other uses. Old car tyres are turned into bags and boots, and very little is thrown away.

Everyone can do something to help reduce the amount of waste that humans produce. We all need to think carefully about what we use, and keep our planet a wonderful place to live.

REDUCE, REUSE AND RECYCLE

1. Decide which one sentence is the most important in each paragraph and copy them here.

Paragraph 1 _____

_____

Paragraph 2 _____

_____

Paragraph 3 _____

_____

Paragraph 4 _____

_____

Paragraph 5 _____

_____

Paragraph 6 _____

_____

2. Draw pictures to show four different ways we dispose of waste.

3. Read the second paragraph again, and underline/highlight the most important points. Now rewrite the paragraph in your own words on the back of this sheet, using only about 100 words. Try to make sure you include all the key information.

4. What is the text explaining about? Put a ✓ or a ✘ in each box.

What happens to our rubbish. ☐   **How we can reduce waste.** ☐

How to make recycled paper. ☐   **What to do about litter.** ☐

5. "Many people believe that our rubbish is slowly killing our planet." Why has the writer used this as her first sentence? Draw a ring round the correct answer.

      To frighten   **To grab the**   **To persuade people that**
        people   **reader's attention**   **rubbish is dangerous.**

6. Find and copy the words or phrases in the text that are nearest in meaning to the following.

A large hole in the ground that waste is dumped into _____

To rot down _____

A machine that burns waste _____

To make new things from used materials _____

Something that is, or used to be, living _____

To get rid of something _____

7. List three different ways that we can help to reduce the amount of waste in the world.

    1. _____

    _____

    2. _____

    _____

    3. _____

    _____